ELLERB

A SPORADIC DIARY COMIC

MARC ELLERBY

15 MAY 2007

PUBLISHED BY GREAT BEAST COMICS

ISBN: 9780957431805

ELLERBISMS

FIRST PRINTING NOVEMBER 2012

PRINTED IN LITHUANIA.

PUBLISHED BY GREAT BEAST COMICS, MANCHESTER, UK
PUBLISHERS: ADAM CADWELL AND MARC ELLERBY

TO VIEW OUR CATALOGUE PLEASE VISIT
WWW.GREATBEASTCOMICS.COM

FOR ANNA.
2015

JUST SO YOU KNOW....

A QUICK WORD ABOUT THIS BOOK.

I STARTED DRAWING **ELLERBISMS** IN MAY 2007, WHICH AT THE TIME OF WRITING THIS IS **FIVE YEARS AGO**. WHICH, IS, WELL, IT'S JUST CRAZY TO THINK ABOUT THAT SO LETS NOT DWELL ON IT BECAUSE IT KIND OF FREAKS ME OUT.

THE IDEA OF ELLERBISMS ORIGINALLY WAS TO TAKE A MOMENT OF THE DAY, NO MATTER HOW TRIVIAL OR SMALL IT SEEMED, AND ILLUSTRATE IT AS A COMIC IN A MOLESKINE SKETCHBOOK. AND TO BEGIN WITH, THAT WAS ALL FINE AND DANDY, BECAUSE IT'S PRETTY EASY DRAWING A COMIC ABOUT WHAT'S FOR DINNER. BUT THEN I MET A SWEDISH GIRL CALLED ANNA AND THEN, WELL, THINGS STOPPED BEING SO SPORADIC (AND BORING).

WHEN I WAS COLLATING THE STRIPS FOR THIS COLLECTION THERE WAS ONE THING THAT BUGGED ME A WHOLE BUNCH: THE EARLY STRIPS ARE PRETTY ROPEY AND THEY'RE NOT A TRUE REPRESENTATION OF WHAT ELLERBISMS BECAME. BECAUSE THE PROJECT BECAME SO MUCH ABOUT ME AND ANNA IT SEEMED A NATURAL CHOICE TO MAKE THE BOOK ABOUT OUR LIFE TOGETHER AND SO SOME STRIPS WENT IN THE PROVERBIAL BIN. SO IF YOU'RE AN OLD FAN OF THE SERIES YOU MAY HAVE HAD A FLICK THROUGH AND WONDERED WHY THERE'S A WHOLE CHUNK MISSING FROM THE START. WELL, IT'S BECAUSE ~~I CAN'T EVEN LOOK AT THOSE STRIPS~~ THEY ADD NOTHING TO THE BIGGER PICTURE OR THE STORY I WANTED TO TELL.

ALSO WHILE DRAWING THE COMIC, THE NATURE OF ILLUSTRATING A SINGULAR MOMENT OF THE DAY MEANT THAT I COULD DIP IN AND OUT OF MY LIFE WITHOUT REALLY GIVING MUCH REASON OR BACKSTORY TO THE STRIPS. THIS AT THE TIME WAS A BLESSING BUT IN HINDSIGHT A HINDRANCE. SO I'VE TRIED TO "FILL IN THE BLANKS" WITH SOME STRIPS THAT MAY HAVE LACKED CONTEXT. JUST WITHOUT HINDERING OR MANIPULATING THE ORIGINAL STORYLINE.

SO WITH THAT COMES A DISCLAIMER!

THESE NEW STRIPS HAVE BEEN DRAWN MANY YEARS (AGAIN, NOT GONNA THINK ABOUT THAT) AFTER THE EVENT TOOK PLACE. SO WHEREAS THE INFORMATION IS AS ACCURATE AS I CAN REMEMBER AND I HAVE NOT FICTIONALISED ANYTHING, THE BRAIN CAN ONLY REMEMBER SO MUCH. I HAVE TRIED TO BE FAIR AND BALANCED WITH THE BOOK BUT HOPEFULLY YOU UNDERSTAND THAT THIS STORY IS FROM MY PERSPECTIVE AND HOW I INTERPRETED EVENTS.

IF YOU'RE KEEN TO SEE THE ORIGINAL RUN OF ELLERBISMS THEN I SUGGEST YOU HEAD TO ELLERBISMS.COM WHERE EVERYTHING HAS BEEN PRESERVED FOR YOU.

SAYING THAT, IF YOU'VE NEVER READ AN ELLERBISMS COMIC BEFORE, WELL IGNORE MOST OF ALL THAT AND ENJOY IT ALREADY!

MARC ELLERBY
THE CHILLY END OF SUMMER 2012.

ELLERBISMS

ell•er•bisms

(NOT 'ELLERYISMS', 'ELLDERBISMS', 'ELLERELLYBISMS' OR SIMILIAR WORDS THAT MAKE ZERO SENSE.)

PROLOGUE

GATWICK AIRPORT
24TH JULY 2007
I DON'T WANT TO SAY I WAS BEING EMO BUT THAT'S EXACTLY WHAT I WAS DOING.
SITTING IN AN AIRPORT, THINKING OF GIRLS.

HOPEFULLY THIS BOOK WON'T COME ACROSS AS A "CLICHÉ TOLD IN PICTURES," IT'S JUST THAT THIS STORY DOES START WITH A GIRL.
HUFF
PD JAMES
PETE JA NOT DEAD
TRAIL OF

WELL... GIRLS. BUT WE'LL GET TO THAT.
ENGLISH
ILETS

THE AFOREMENTIONED GIRL IS **ANNA**. THE GIRL I CAN'T HAVE.
Rankin
Rankin

CRIME
OR MAYBE SHE'S THE GIRL I'M AFRAID TO HAVE.

THE SWEDISH GOTH GIRL WHO I WORK WITH AND HAS A BOYFRIEND
AND SHE'S KIND OF ONE OF MY BOSSES.

ON PAPER, SHE SHOULDN'T BE THE GIRL I'M OBSESSING OVER.

THE GIRL, WHO WHEN WE FIRST MET, WE HATED EACH OTHER.

THAT ANNA IS SUCH A SUCK UP.

WHO'S THAT GEEK IN THE SKINNY JEANS?

BUT SLOWLY...

...AND SURELY...
IS IT WRONG TO HAVE MISSED YOU THIS MUCH WHEN YOU'RE NOT IN WORK?

...SHE'S THE GIRL WHO GOT STUCK IN MY MIND.

BUT THEN SHE'S NOT THE ONLY GIRL CLOUDING MY THOUGHTS...

MY BEST FRIEND, SOPHIE, WHO I'M INADVERTENTLY MESSING AROUND, WHERE FRIENDSHIP HAS BECOME CONFUSED WITH SOMETHING ELSE.
BRIGHTON PIER
I'M NOT SURE WHAT I WANT AND I COULD RUIN A FRIENDSHIP FOREVER.
I KNOW I'LL END UP HURTING HER.
IT'S GONE TOO FAR TO GO BACK TO THE WAY IT WAS.

SOME WOULD SAY A TRIP ABROAD MIGHT DO ME SOME GOOD...

A BIT OF ALONE TIME.
A CHANCE TO THINK.
A MUCH-NEEDED BREATHER.
Mirror
NOW WHAT

ONLY THING IS, I'M HEADING TO THE SAN DIEGO COMIC CON WHERE 30,000 PEOPLE ATTEND EACH YEAR.

THAT "CHANCE TO THINK" MAY HAVE TO WAIT...

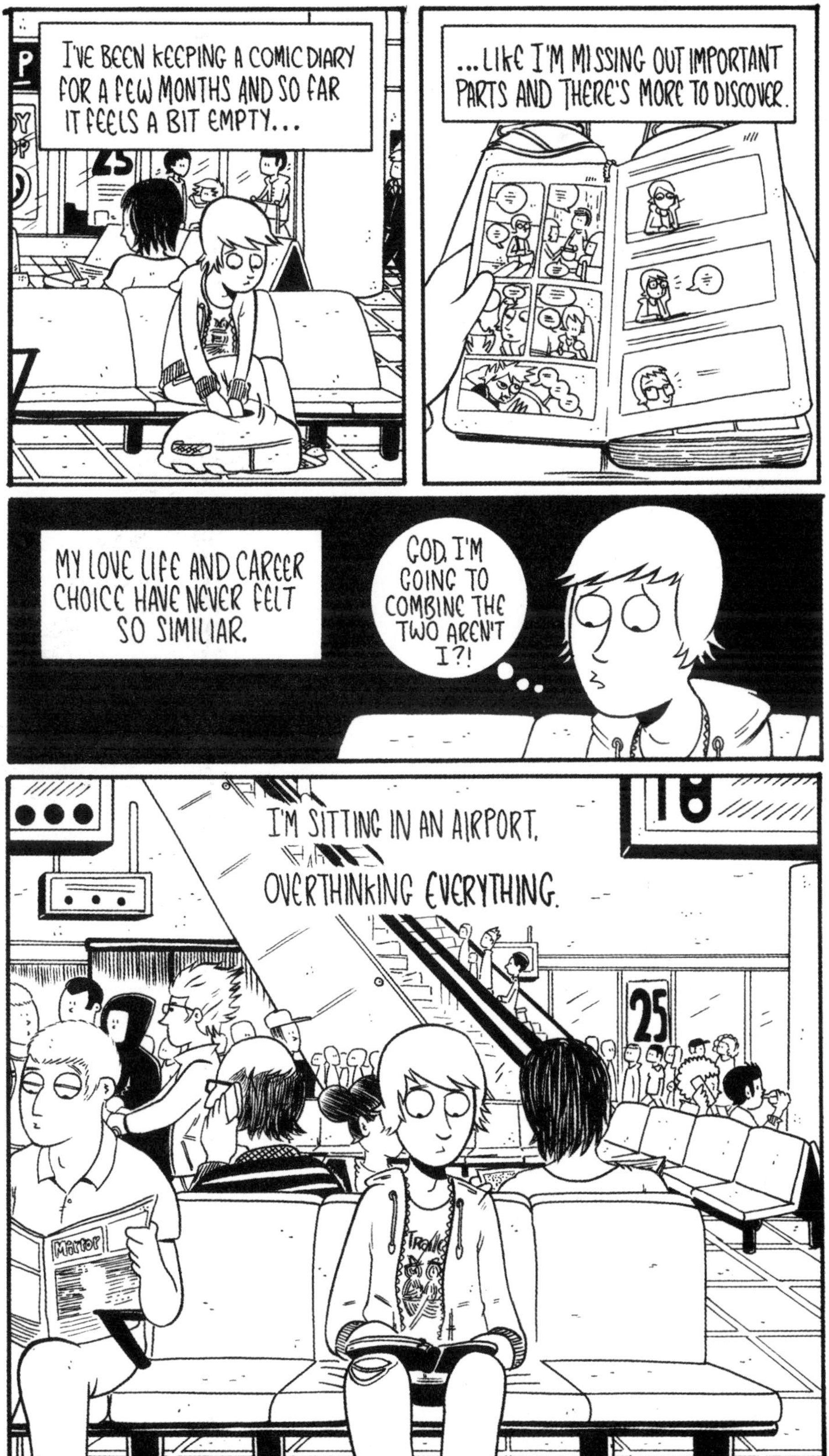

I'M SITTING IN AN AIRPORT.

OVERTHINKING EVERYTHING.

CHAPTER ONE

SAN DIEGO COMICON PART ONE
25 JUL 2007
MAYBE WE SHOULDN'T WAKE HIM?
SHHH, LET ME GET MY CAMERA.
OH.
HEY...
Trail of Dead
YOU'RE SO CUTE WHEN YOU'RE SLEEPING.
OH THIS IS SO WEIRD... I WAS HAVING THIS REALLY GOOD DREAM ABOUT PAPER...
...I MEAN... HELLO.

SDCC PT 2 - BREAKFAST

26 JUL 2007

SDCCPT3 - DISASTER STRIKES
27 JUL 2007
I CAN'T BELIEVE WE JUST JUMPED A TRAIN.*
QUICK, RUN. BEFORE "THEY" GET US!!
TRIP
?
OH MY GOD!
OUCH
SHIT! MARC, ARE YOU OKAY?
FSSSSSSS
HAHA! LOOK AT YOUR FACE! WHERE'S MY CAMERA?
YOU LOOK LIKE A JAMES KOCHALKA DRAWING!
FSSSSSSS
* A STATIONARY FREIGHT TRAIN, AT THAT...

SDCC PT4 - YOU DRUNK BASTARD... 28 JUL 2007

HEY MARC.

OH HI, MAN.

DUDE YOU SO MADE MY NIGHT LAST NIGHT!

LAST NIGHT...

OH, ONI HAVE ALL THE COOL PEOPLE WORKING FOR THEM!

BRIAN WOOD, BRANON GRAHAM, COREY LEWIS, DEAN TRIPPE...

I'M DEAN TRIPPE!

YOU'RE DEAN TRIPPE?

I'M DEAN TRIPPE!

YOU'RE DEAN TRIPPE!

28 JUL 2007

RING
RING
RING
RING
14:13
Incoming
Sophie
HUH?
RING
RING!
HELLO?
HI!
YOU'RE CALLING ME.
I AM.
312
ARE YOU SURE? IT'S EXPENSIVE.
OH I DON'T MIND, I JUST WANTED TO TALK TO YOU.
I'VE MISSED YOU.
HEY. YEAH YOU TOO.
SO. WHAT HAVE YOU BEEN UP TO?
OH. Y'KNOW. THIS. THAT...

SDCC PT5- CONVENTION CATCHPHRASE. 29 JUL 2007

SDCC PT 6 - RETURN TO SENDER

30 JUL 2007

FLYING BACK HOME, CRAMPED IN MY SEAT WITH A BANDAGED AND STINGING FOOT...

...A SOGGY, ODD-SMELLING MEAL IS FLUNG ON MY TABLE. IT'S STEAK AND MASH (APPARENTLY...)

...EMOTIONALLY DRAINED AND PHYSICALLY EXHAUSTED, MY BEST BET IS TO SLEEP 'TIL LONDON, HOPING EVERYTHING GOES AWAY.

3 1 JUL 2007

ock University Hospital
ersity Hospit

RING
RING.
15.20
Anna
Answer
Decline

HEY.
HEY. WHAT DID THEY SAY?
Basildo
Ba
THE BLOOD BROTHERS

IT'S NOT BROKEN, JUST REALLY SPRAINED.
THEY BANDAGED ME UP AND SENT ME ON MY WAY.

WELL THAT'LL TEACH YOU NOT TO GET SO BLOODY DRUNK.
BUT I LIKE IT!

SO HEY, THIS IS THE FIRST TIME WE'VE SPOKEN ON THE PHONE.
IT IS. I THOUGHT IT WOULD BE WEIRD BUT IT'S REALLY NOT.

NO, IT FEELS NORMAL. SO ARE YOU WORKING TOMORROW?
THE BLOOD BROTHERS

YEAH WE'RE BOTH ON THE LATE SHIFT...
...I KINDA CAN'T WAIT.

ME NEITHER.

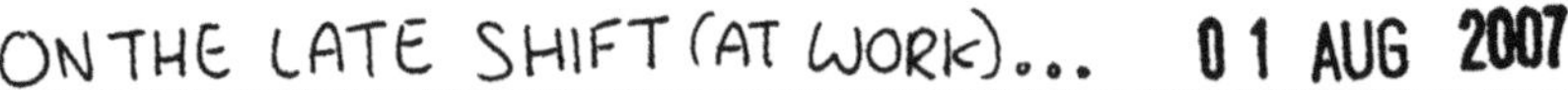
ON THE LATE SHIFT (AT WORK)... 01 AUG 2007

HEY! HOW WAS SAN DIEGO?

WELL, MY FOOT'S GONE **PURPLE** AND I'M MORE EXHAUSTED THAN I'VE BEEN IN MY **ENTIRE** LIFE AND I CAN'T WAIT TO GET OFF THIS **STUPID** ISLAND AND GO BACK TO THE BLOODY STATES.

WELL, YOU GUYS ARE GONNA HAVE **FUN** TONIGHT.

03 AUG 2007

YOU'RE ALWAYS DOING THIS TO ME, MARC...
.. ALWAYS MESSING ME ABOUT.
I'M, I'M NOT ALWAYS DOING THIS TO YOU.
SOPHIE, I'M SORRY, BUT I DON'T WANT A RELATIONSHIP WITH YOU.
WHY?! WHAT'S CHANGED?!
NOTHING AND THAT'S JUST IT...
... I STILL SEE YOU ONLY AS A FRIEND.

HOW LONG ARE YOU GOING FOR?
URR. FIVE DAYS? YEAH FIVE DAYS.
YOU LOOKING FORWARD TO IT?
Dublin
CITY GUIDE
YEAH, IT'LL BE GOOD TO GET AWAY.
YOU JUST GOT BACK!
HA, I KNOW, RIGHT?
SO, WHO ARE YOU GOING WITH?
BEEP.
MY FRIEND RACHEL. HER BROTHER. HIS GIRLFRIEND AND THEIR FRIENDS.
YOUR FRIEND RACHEL...
...WHO IS A GIRL.
IT'S NOT LIKE THAT!
HMM.

20 AUG 2007
DUBLIN!
YOU KNOW, I DON'T THINK I'VE EVER SEEN YOU DRUNK, BEFORE.
I'M NOT DRUNK!
I'M JUST SORTA

DUBLIN: OH JAMES...

21 AUG 2007

ALSO, HAPPY BIRTHDAY, MUM!

DUBLIN

23 AUG 2007

25 AUG 2007

WATCHING ARCADE FIRE ON T.V

OH ANNA YOU ARE **SO** MUCH FUN!
YOU'RE LIKE A BLOODY... SLINKY!
OR SOMETHING.
HA HA HA HA!
A SLINKY? WHAT?
WELL YOU KNOW. YOU GO DOWN STAIRS, YOU'RE ONE LONG PIECE OF WIRE AND
COUGH

09 SEP 2007

HEY MARK.
HELLO YOUNG MARC HOW ARE YOU DEAR BOY?
DR WHO
OH NOT SO BAD, ANNA'S IN SWEDEN SO...
...I'M MISSING HER A--
OH MY GOD!
SOMETHING TO PLAY WITH WHILE I'M AWAY!!
XXX
OH MY GOD!
?

10 SEP 2007

YEAH, I MISS YOU TOO.
LIKE A LOT.
I WAS TELLING MY MUM ALL ABOUT YOU...
"YOU'D LIKE HER, SHE'S NOT INSANE."
AWW, WOW, THAT'S KINDA WEIRD TO THINK YOU TALK ABOUT ME.
I CAN'T IMAGINE WHAT YOU'D SAY...
"SHE'S A GOTH... AND A SHIT."
"SHE LAUGHS AT ALL MY JOKES THOUGH."

ME AND TOM ARE 24 YEARS OLD... 12 SEP 2007

...TOM HAS A MORTGAGE

15 SEP 2007

SO *MUNCH* YEAH, SUPERBAD'S MON AT *CHOMP* 8·30
ARE YOU EATING WHILE YOU'RE ON THE PHONE TO ME?
CHOMP MWHAT?
YOU ARE! WHAT ARE YOU EATING?!?
A CRISP.
AND THAT SERIOUSLY COULDN'T HAVE WAITED 'TIL AFTER YOU RANG?
CHOMP
WHAT IS WRONG WITH YOU?!
ROLO TOMASSI

18 OCT 2007
HEY, YOU'RE SUPPOSED TO BE FOLDING...
YEAH, BUT I GUESS KISSING YOU IS LOADS MORE FUN.
YOU "GUESS?"

RE: "I MIGHTMOVE BACK TO SWEDEN" 21 OCT 2007

LOOK, SO I DON'T CARE BECAUSE I PROB -ABLY REALLY LIKE YOU.

WELL I GUESS I MIGHT BE IN LOVE WITH YOU.

A LITTLE.

IN THEORY.

ONE DAY.

MAYBE.

A POSSIBILITY, YOU KNOW.

THE--

SHHH.

LES SAVY FAV @ SCALA, LONDON 22 OCT 2007

23 OCT 2007

* THIS IS BEING DRAWN IN JUNE 2008!

04 NOV 2007

ACTUALLY, DID YOU TELL THEM OR JUST, Y'KNOW, "ANNA-TELL" THEM?

WELL, Y'KNOW, WHEN YOU'RE CONVINCED YOU'VE TOLD PEOPLE WHAT YOU WANTED TO SAY, BUT IN REALITY YOU GIVE THEM VAGUE INFORMATION, LETTING THEM GUESS AND END UP NOT TELLING THEM ANYTHING?

RUSSIA
TURKEY
U.S.A
TOKYOPO
TRAVEL WRI
ROUGH GUIDE
ROUGHGUIDE TO
Sweden
Sweden
UHHHR...
OH!
UHHHR...
OH!

THOUGHT BUBBLE COMIC-CON. LEEDS
10 NOV 2007
WHAT WAS THAT FILM WITH BUGS BUNNY AND MICHAEL JORDAN?
MUNCH SPACE JAM.
OH YEAH! SPACE JAM! I LOVE THAT FILM!
DUTCH
OH ME TOO! IT'S SO GOOD!
SWEDISH
REALLY?
BLOODY EUROPEANS!

LEEDS - 3am

11 NOV 2007

OMG!
WHAT?
GREGGS
TRY OUR NEW
TUNA MAYO
MADE FRESH GREGGS
THE GREGGS HERE ARE OPEN 24 HOURS!
AND THEY TOTALLY HAVE A BOUNCER ON THE DOOR!?
AND SMASH PROOF GLASS IN FRONT OF THE COUNTER!?
WELCOME TO THE NORTH...

14 NOV 2007

HEROES
15 NOV 2007
OH I GET IT. THIS CLARE GIRL IS BASICALLY WOLVERINE, WHAT WITH THE HEALING POWERS AND SHIT...
ARE YOU THE ONE? SAVING YOU...DID I SAVE THE WORLD?
I DON'T KNOW. I'M JUST THE CHEERLEADER!
TSK! "I'M JUST THE CHEERLEADER", BUB!
SHUDDUP.

THE DARJEELING LIMITED

27 NOV 2007

14 DEC 2007

GOD. JUST WHAT DO YOU GET NANS FOR CHRISTMAS?
MY NAN'S DEAD.
TSK. ALRIGHT, WHAT DO I GET MY NAN FOR CHRISTMAS? JESUS!

TEACHING...

28 JAN 2008

BUYING NEW SHOES...
29 JAN 2008
I QUITE LIKE THESE ONES, WHAT DO YOU THINK?
HA HA HA!
WHAT?
YOU LOOK LIKE A DUCK!

CHAPTER TWO

KITCHEN
BOOKS
ANNA
EPS

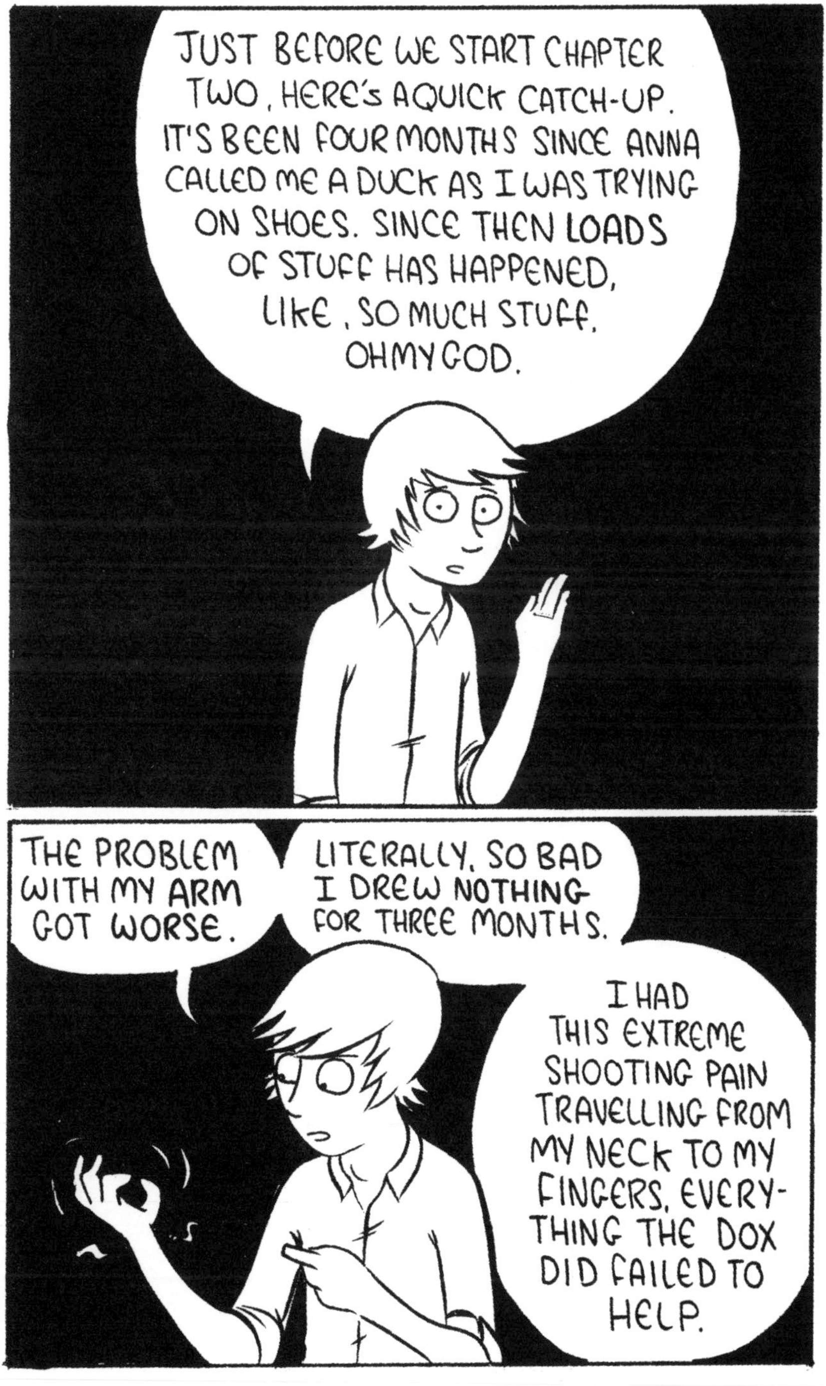

JUST BEFORE WE START CHAPTER TWO, HERE'S A QUICK CATCH-UP. IT'S BEEN FOUR MONTHS SINCE ANNA CALLED ME A DUCK AS I WAS TRYING ON SHOES. SINCE THEN LOADS OF STUFF HAS HAPPENED, LIKE, SO MUCH STUFF. OHMYGOD.

TURNS OUT THE PROBLEM WASN'T EVEN IN MY ARM, IT WAS ALL TO DO WITH MY SHOULDER!
I SAW A LOVELY PHYSIOTHERAPIST CALLED TOBY WHO IRONED EVERYTHING OUT. *MPH*
SHHH.
AFTER THE COURSE, I WAS FULLY DRAWING AGAIN AND AS IF BY MAGIC MY DRAWING HAD MAJORLY IMPROVED!
THANKS TOBY!
IN THIS TIME MY DAD FELL ILL AND HAD TO HAVE AN OPERATION.
THE VALVES IN HIS HEART WERE CLOGGED BY 35 YEARS OF SMOKE AND A BAD DIET.

IT WAS HORRIBLE TO HAVE TO GO THROUGH. THOUGH IT DID BRING US CLOSER TOGETHER.
FOR THE FIRST TIME IN MY LIFE I THOUGHT ABOUT WHAT IT'D BE LIKE WITHOUT MY DAD...
...AND IT SCARED ME.
I'M JUST GLAD HE'S OKAY.
ANNA AND I GOT CLOSER, TOO.
I BROUGHT YOU SOME TEA.
OH, TA. THIS MONOLOGUING IS PRETTY HARD WORK.

ANNA WAS SUCH A ROCK. MY DAD'S HEALTH. MY WRIST PROBLEMS. ALL THAT WAS GETTING TOO MUCH AND I COULDN'T HAVE COPED WITHOUT HER.
SHE'S PRETTY COOL, RIGHT?
AND ALTHOUGH WE HADN'T BEEN TOGETHER THAT LONG IT FELT I WAS IN IT FOR THE LONG RUN.
EVEN THOUGH ON THE SURFACE WE WERE COMPLETE OPPOSITES,(SHE'S A BIT OF A GOTH)INSIDE WE WEREN'T THAT DIFFERENT.
I'M NOT A GOTH!
WE LAUGHED AN AWFUL LOT TOGETHER.
LOL.
WE HAD ARGUMENTS THAT WERE "MAYBE" STARTED BY ME.
RAA RAA.
I STARTED FALLING MADLY IN LOVE.
MY SWEDISH BEAUTY.
ALL MINE.

THE COMIC WORLD STARTED PAYING MORE ATTENTION TO ME.
HA! PENGUINS!
MY CHEMICAL ROMANCE
POLAR OPPOSITES
I BECAME FRUSTRATED WORKING ON "LOVE THE WAY YOU LOVE." THE WORLD SEEMED MORE INTERESTED IN MY OWN MINI COMICS.
I JUST WANTED IT TO BE FINISHED, BUT WHEN IT WAS, I WAS REALLY SAD.
I'M NEVER GOING TO DRAW THESE CHARACTERS AGAIN.
SOB
IT WAS LIKE THE END OF ONE CHAPTER AND THE START OF ANOTHER.
Photoshop
op document
ovetheway60.jpg
closing?
ncel
Save
I ATTENDED THE UK WEB & MINI COMIC THING CON IN MARCH AND HAD A REALLY GREAT TIME.
HOW MUCH IS THIS?
WHAT'S THIS ABOUT?
HA! PENGUINS!
ELLERBISMS

I THINK THERE I FELT IT WAS TIME TO DO MY OWN THING AND GIVE IT A REAL PUSH.
THAT'S £3.
THAT ONE'S ABOUT AN EX-GIRL FRIEND.
YEAH, I KNOW. LOL PENGUINS, RIGHT?
IT WAS ALSO GREAT TO HANG OUT WITH MY NEW PARTNER IN COMIC CRIME, ADAM CADWELL.
IF YOU LIKE MY STUFF YOU SHOULD TRY ADAM'S.
ONLY MINE'S BETTER.
PRICE LIST
IN APRIL, ANNA AND I STARTED TO LOOK AT FLATS TOGETHER.
Marc says
what about this one?
Marc says
http://www.ri
Anna says
Mmm. I don'
TAP TAP TAP
TAP TAP
IT TOOK A BIT OF CONVINCING ON MY PART BUT WHEN WE STARTED LOOKING WE FOUND A PLACE STRAIGHT AWAY.
DO YOU LIKE IT?
YEAH.
DO YOU?
SHALL WE GO FOR IT?
I DUNNO.
SHOULD WE?
c2c

COME TO SIGN THE CONTRACT I STARTED FREAKING OUT.
I'M BEING PUSHED!
(I WASN'T)
I'M SCARED!
(I WASN'T)
WHAT IF YOU HATE ME?
(OH, SHUT UP)
MAY 1ST WE MOVED IN TOGETHER.
WHERE SHALL I PUT THIS?
UHHHHR.
CDS
AND WITH ALL THAT OUT OF THE WAY, HERE IS CHAPTER TWO.

01 MAY 2008
I'M SO GLAD WE'VE DONE THIS.
I'M GLAD I CONVINCED YOU TO DO THIS.

02 MAY 2008

Z
CREAAAK
STOMP
UGH WHAT THE FUCK IS THAT?
I DUNNO. IT MUST BE UPSTAIRS
STOMP!
WHAT, DO WE HAVE **IRON MAN** LIVING ABOVE US?

0 5 MAY 2008

OOH. I'M TOO DISTRACTED BY YOU TO DRAW!
AW.
THAT AND I CAN'T WAIT TO SEE IRON MAN LATER.
DUNNN DUNNN
DUN DUN DUN!
DUNNA DUNNA DUN
DUN DUN DUN DUNN!
MMM HMM

BRISTOL COMIC CON PART ONE 09 MAY 2008
MARC...
ADAM.
I JUST CALLED BRYAN TALBOT BRYAN GORMAN!
I SAID THAT HE RECITED SOME POETRY TO ME AT THOUGHT BUBBLE AND HE SAID "BRYAN TALBOT DID, NOT BRYAN GORMAN!"
WHO WOULD DO THAT, MARC?
WHO'S BRYAN GORMAN!?
ADAM CADWELL APPEARS COURTESY OF THEEVERYDAY.ADAMCADWELL.COM

BRISTOL COMIC CON PART TWO 10 MAY 2008

BRISTLOL COMIC CON PART THREE 10 MAY 2008
WHY ISN'T ANYONE COMING TO OUR TABLE, MARC?
LIKE, WHAT DO THEY WANT FROM US?
WELL, THEY JUST TAKE ONE LOOK AT OUR STUFF AND GO "THIS ISN'T BLEACH" AND LEAVE.
LOOK AT 'EM...
"THIS ISN'T BLEACH."
JOHN CEI DOUGLAS APPEARS COURTESY OF WWW.SHOTFORMEAT.COM

BRISTOL COMIC CON PART FOUR .10 MAY 2008

BRISTOL COMIC CON PART FIVE 10 MAY, 2008

BRISTOL COMIC CON PART SIX 11 MAY 2008

12 MAY 2008

DON'T YOU EVER SPEAK TO ME LIKE THAT AGAIN.
I'M SORRY...
...GOD, I REALLY AM.
I KNOW...
...I KNOW.

16 MAY 2008

20 MAY 2008

OH! OH! AND I WANT TO GO TO THE LIBRARY!
YEAH, YEAH I WANT TO GET SOME HORROR BOOKS OUT!
HEY GIMME A PIGGY BACK!
OH!
GO!
UHHRM...

24 MAY 2008

YOU MAKE ME FEEL SO STUPID, SOMETIMES.
NO, I DON'T.
I JUST FEEL LIKE I'M CONSTANTLY DOING OR SAYING EVERYTHING WRONG WITH YOU.
BUT YOU'RE NOT.
NO, I'M JUST SAYING, THAT'S HOW IT FEELS.

29 MAY 2008

OH YEAH, SEE HOW HE RUNS FROM YOU!
COMMITMENT ISSUES!
IN 15 YEARS TIME, YOU'LL LOOK AT EACH OTHER AND IN A MOMENT OF SHEER STUPIDITY, YOU'LL MAKE A HUGE MIS-TAKE AND RUIN YEARS OF FRIENDSHIP!
SEE THE SIGNS!
UHHR, YOU'RE NOT TALKING ABOUT A PAST EXPERIENCE ARE YOU?
NO!
I MEAN ...
... NO ...

ELECTRIC TOOTHBRUSH "FUN."

02 JUN 2008

BZZZZ

ZNNNNNN

BZZZZZZ

BZZZZZZ

BZZZZZZ

AAAAAAHH

I HAD TO STOP USING IT BECAUSE OF MY RSI... LAME.

11 JUN 2008
JESSOPS IS FULL OF FUCKING MORONS.
HEY, CAN I GET SOME INK FOR THE EPSON R1800? MATTE BLACK & YELLOW, PLEASE?
DO YOU KNOW WHICH ONE IT IS?
YEAH, THE ONE WITH THE FROG ON THE BOX.
THEY'VE ALL GOT FROGS ON THEM.
...THE ONES NEXT TO THE PENGUINS.
ARE YOU SURE?
...YES!
O.M.F.G

12 JUN 2008

SO, I DON'T GET IT. IS THE HULK, LIKE, ACTUALLY INSIDE HIM?
AMY, THE HULK IS ALWAYS INSIDE BRUCE BANNER, IT'S A MENTAL AND PHYSICAL STRUGGLE...
HE'S VERY ANGRY ABOUT IT...
DESIGN
VERY! ANGRY!

CHAPTER THREE

Välkommen till Sverige* 14 JUN 2008

*(or 'Welcome to Sweden')

SWEDEN. YEAH!
15 JUN 2008
I GUESS A PART OF OUR LOVE IS THAT WE HAVE SUCH A "COMPANIONSHIP" TOGETHER.
YEAH, LIKE IF ONE OF US IS SAD, THEN IN FIVE MINUTES THE OTHER ONE IS SAD, TOO.
IT'S LIKE, YOU SMILE THEN I SMILE, TOO.
IT'S A GOOD THING...
...I GUESS.

SWEDEN: MARC LEARNS A NEW WORD. 16 JUN 2008

SWEDEN: DAY BEFORE WE LEAVE
WAKE UP, CUDDLE.
HEY.
BREAKFAST.
YES?
SMÖRGÅSBORD.
REINDEER!
OM!
ZOO
IT'S A BEAR!
SEALS!
IT'S A SEAL!
COMIC LIBRARY!!!
SHONEN JUMP
OOO OOO OOO OOH.
LOADS OF TAIYO MATSUMOTO BOOKS.
OH, I'VE NEVER SEEN ANY OF THESE BEFORE.
DECLARATIONS...
I THINK I'VE FALLEN EVEN MORE IN LOVE WITH YOU THIS WEEK.
CAFÉ
OH THESE ARE LOOKING SO GOOD, MARC.
OM.

17 JUN 2008

MAKE OUT.
MEET WITH SOFIA.
COMICS.
COMICS.
COMICS.
TRAIN
IT'S LIKE 11PM AND IT'S STILL LIGHT OUT.
FOREST
WOW
MAJA.
PURRR.
INTERNET.
"LOVE THE WAY YOU LOVE, AN UTTER WASTE OF ELLERBY'S TALENTS AND DEVOID OF LIFE."
OH COME ON!
ANNA'S CAT ALLERGY
ATCHOO!
PORTABLE DOOR
SLEEP.
Z.

BACK TO NORMALITY.
19 JUN 2008
M
TR
FOOTBALL BOOK
TENNIS BOOK
ZZZZZ BOOK
BOOK BOOK
SIGH...
RAAA RAA RAA
SIGH...
CLICK.
HUFF.
WE DON'T WANT TO BE HERE, DO WE?
NO.

ANNA'S BIRTHDAY
22 JUN 2008
OH, WOW!
OH, YOU DIDN'T?!
ABSOLUTE SANDMAN VOLUME TWO
I DID!
THIS BEACH IS TOO WINDY.
HAHA HAHA.
WHAT?
LOOK AT MARC'S HAIR!
I CAN'T CONTROL IT!
WHOEVER'S INDY, GET SHORTSTOP TO GO IN THE HOLE!
SHORTSTOP?!

25 JUN 2008

I LOVE THE WAY THESE WASHING TABLETS MAKE OUR CLOTHES SMELL.
THE SMITHS
OH. I'M **SO** NOT GAY.
MMM.

26 JUN 2008

OH, CAN WE WATCH THE SEX AND THE CITY TRIPLE BILL?
I'M STILL NOT GAY.
UH-HUH.

SMASHBROS BRAWL...
04 JUL 2008
PRESS START.
BUT I DON'T WANNA PLAY ANYMORE.
WELL I WANT A
REMATCH!
BABY...
OH, JUST GIVE ME THE CONTROLLER!
BABY!

17 JUL 2008

SHALL I TURN THE LIGHT OUT, PETAL?
STAR WARS
WHY HAVE YOU STARTED CALLING ME "PETAL"?
STAR WARS
CLICK
IT'S LIKE SAYING "HELLO LEAF".
OR "HELLO GRASS."
GRASS ISN'T PART OF THE FLOWER, THOUGH.
STAR WARS
UHHRM... "HELLO LEAF?"
STAR

20 JUL 2008
IT JUST FEELS LIKE I'M WAITING FOR YOU TO MOVE OUT.
I DON'T WANT TO THOUGH.
I DUNNO HOW MUCH MORE I CAN CONVINCE YOU.
MAYBE YOU CAN'T.

WHATEVER AND EVER, AMEN.
21 JUL 2008
GIVE ME MY MONEY BACK!
CUT
GIVE ME MY MONEY BACK!
YOU BITCH!
I WAN'T MY MONEY BACK!
CUCUMBER?
AND DO-N'T FOR-GET
NO, THANKS
AND DO-N'T FOR-GET.
TO GIVE ME BACK MY BLACK T-SHIRT!
LUNCH IS DONE.
'KAY.

22 JUL 2008

JAGUAR LOVE, 100 CLUB, LONDON...

LA LALALALA

LALALA

C'MON!

LALALALA

LA LALALALALA

LALA LALA

UGH. WHAT ARE YOU DOING?

RACHEL'S DISAPPOINTED WITH ME AS ALWAYS.

THE DARK FUCKIN' KNIGHT
27 JUL 2008
HOW ABOUT A MAGIC TRICK?
I'M GONNA MAKE THIS PENCIL DISAPPEAR.
PERCY PIGS
Coke
THUD!
DUH DAH!
IT'S... IT'S, AH, GONE!
THIS IS THE BEST THING, EVER.

04 AUG 2008

HAVE YOU ACTUALLY BEEN TO NEW YORK?
I ♡ NY
NO...
I ♡ NY
• • •
I ♡ NY
YOU'RE SUCH A HYPOCRITE!
SNIFF.
I ♡ NY

09 AUG 2008
GLORIOUS THINGS I SAID/DID AT MY BIRTHDAY PARTY.
(I'M SORRY HELEN.)
SERIOUSLY, IF ANYONE SAID "COCK" OR "DICK" TO HER...
...HER VAGINA WOULD EXPLODE.
JESUS.
HEY, HELEN! CHECK OUT MY PUBES.
ARGH!
ZIP.
WARIOWARE!
YES!
WHY IS IT DARK?

ANNA'S BIRTHDAY PRESENT TO ME.
10 AUG 2008
R.E.M HELLO
R.E.M
R.E.M
R.E.M
R.E.M
R.E.
TWICKENH
30
PLUS SP
R.E.M
NAH-UH.
R.E.M
NAH UH!
THE VERY GOOD "R.E.M HELLO" IS OUT NOW FROM CHRONICLE BOOKS.

17 AUG 2008

SO, FOR MY MUM'S 50TH I GOT HER A NINTENDO D.S...
BLUE!
HMM.
HER BOYFRIEND, STEVE, GOT HER A VERY EXPENSIVE RING.
OH. IT'S DIFFERENT.
"DIFFERENT!?"
THE PRESENT SHE WAS MOST EXCITED ABOUT THOUGH?
ANNA! ANNA! THE BIRDIES ARE USING THE BIRD TABLE YOU GOT ME!
COME LOOK!

HELLBOY 2

21 AUG 2008

R.E.M@TWICKENHAM
30 AUG 2008
I DON'T KNOW WHY "COUNTRY FEEDBACK" BY R.E.M AFFECTS ME SO MUCH.
HEARING IT IN PERSON FOR THE FIRST TIME IS AN OVER-WHELMING EXPERIENCE
MAYBE IT'S THE SELFISH LYRICAL ASPECT THAT I ASSOCIATE WITH LOW POINTS IN MY LIFE...
I NEED THIS.
...BUT WHEN PETER BUCK GLIDES THROUGH HIS GUITAR SOLO...
...IT'S LIKE HE'S PUTTING MY PAST DEMONS TO REST.
I NEVER THOUGHT I'D EVER HEAR IT LIVE...
...I'M SO GLAD I'M SHARING IT WITH ANNA.

3 1 AUG 2008

OHMYGOD, ANNA MADE THE BEST DUCK STIR FRY LAST NIGHT. SWEAR TO GOD.
I'VE NEVER HAD DUCK BEFORE.
WHAT? OH, MAN IT'S SO NICE!
DUCK'S CRISPY ISN'T IT?
...
WELL, CRISPY DUCK IS.
OH.
PLEASE DON'T PUT THAT IN YOUR COMIC DIARY.
HA!

JAMIE MCKELVIE APPEARS COURTESY OF KIERON GILLEN.

16 SEP 2008

COFFEE, TOOTS?
PLEASE.
OW!
PAPERCUT?
OWWW!
YOU WANT A PLASTER FOR IT?
NAH, I'LL BE ALRIGHT.
LATERZ...
DID YOU EVER WATCH 'CAROLINE IN THE CITY?'
HAHA IS THAT WHAT MADE YOU WANT TO BECOME A CARTOONIST?
OW!
CITRUS JUICE IN YOUR PAPERCUT?
OWWW!

BIRMINGHAM COMIC SHOW '08 PT. ONE 04 OCT 2008

BIRMINGHAM COMIC SHOW PT. TWO

05 OCT 2008

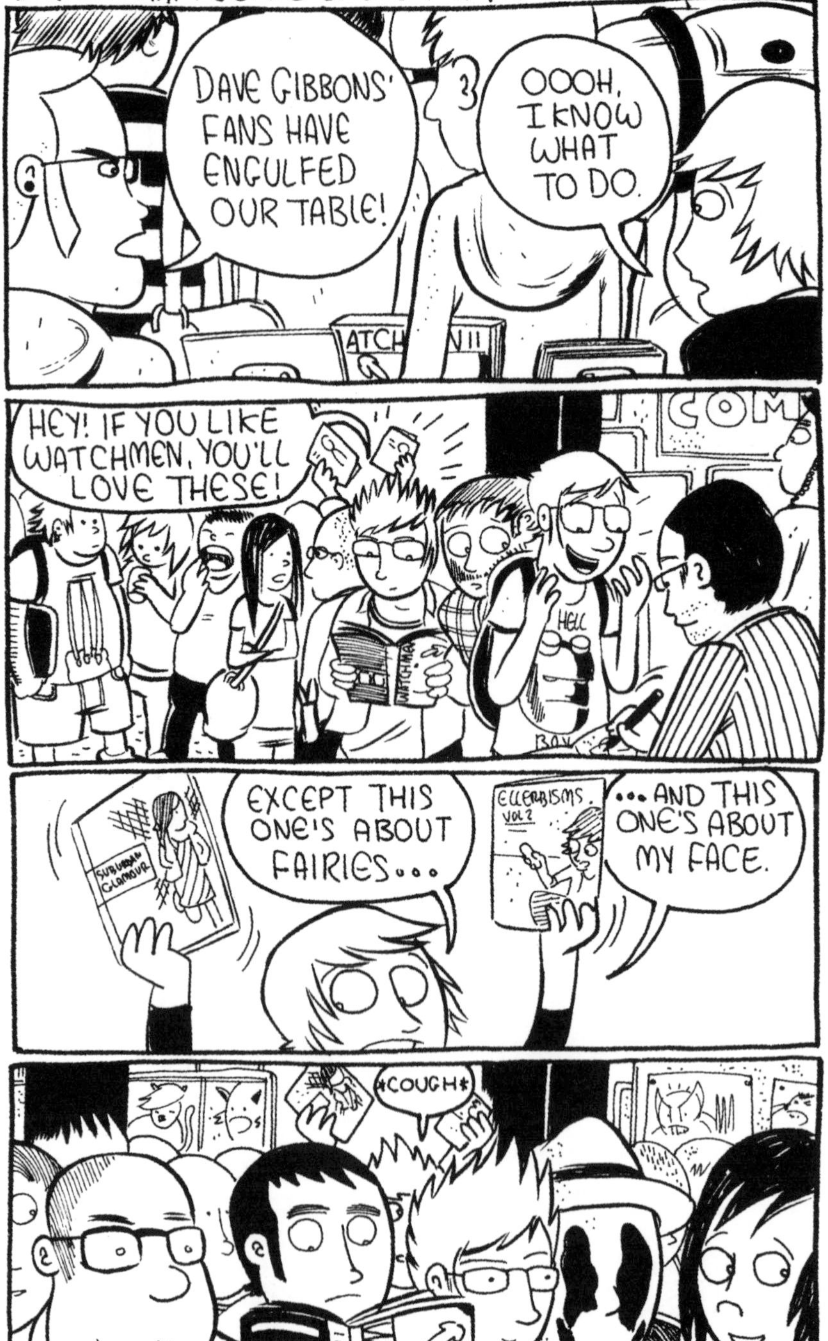

DAVE GIBBONS' FANS HAVE ENGULFED OUR TABLE!

OOOH, I KNOW WHAT TO DO.

HEY! IF YOU LIKE WATCHMEN, YOU'LL LOVE THESE!

EXCEPT THIS ONE'S ABOUT FAIRIES...

...AND THIS ONE'S ABOUT MY FACE.

SUBURBAN GLAMOUR IS OUT NOW FROM IMAGE COMICS.

11 OCT 2008

ME AND BEAR WERE DANCING TO BEN FOLDS' 'THE BITCH WENT NUTS.'

20 OCT 2008

ARE YOU WEARING MY SLIPPERS?
I THINK THIS SHOULD BE THE NEW PHOTO FOR MY WEB-SITE.
WELL. BYE BYE FANS.

0 2 NOV 2008

THOUGHT BUBBLE, SHIT YEAH!!!

SO, HOW MANY GIRLS HAVE YOU **KISSED** IN THIS ONE, THEN?

NOT THAT MANY!

HER?

YES.

HER?

YUP.

NO. NO.

YEAH. ONCE.

HMM-MMM. YES.

NOPE. YES.

SIX!

NOT ALL AT ONCE, THOUGH...

THE EVERYDAY BY ADAM CADWELL IS OUT NOW, YO!

THOUGHT BUBBLE AFTERPARTY. SHIT YEAH!!!
15 NOV 2008
SCARY GO ROUND'S SO POPULAR, I BET, BECAUSE IT'S SO, UNIVERSAL. IT'S, Y'KNOW "T FOR TEEN."
HAHA "T FOR TEEN!"
CADWELL.
JOHN ALLISON.
ANNA WITH REALLY HARD TO DRAW NEW HAIR.
THAT MEANS "TIME OUT" BY THE WAY.
T FOR TEEN!!!
HUH.
FUCKING PENS GAVE ME SHIT, DRAWING THIS ONE
JOHN ALLISON APPEARS COURTESY OF SCARYGOROUND.COM

17 NOV 2008

APPARENTLY I ONLY WORK WITH BALDING PEOPLE...

ROCKGUITARBANDHEROWHATEVER

22 NOV 2008

BACK TO SWEDEN (HOORAY!)
13 DEC 2008
STANSTED AIRPORT.
(DEPARTURES.)
18.05 FR823 SEVILL-
18.10 EZY346 COPENH
18.10 FR058 STOCKHC
18.10 FR107 SHANNON
BING BONG BING
AAAH.
CAN THE PASSENGER WHO COLLECTED THE INCORRECT GREEN SUITCASE FROM THE X30 COACH FROM SOUTHEND PLEASE RETURN IT TO...
HEY, MY CASE IS A GREEN CASE.
. . .
UH OH!

BACK IN SWEDEN
14 DEC 2008
PKAW!
ZZOO
IT'S JUST LIKE SEEING IT AT THE CINEMA!
ZCHO SCTUU
Z.
SCTUU TINGTING
BOOM
SNIFF.
SNIFF.
BOOM
ROW!

STILL IN SWEDEN

15 DEC 2008

CHAPTER FOUR

WE WENT TO SEE TWILIGHT...
20 DEC 2008
MMM. DO I WANT CRISPS?
THAT'S BETWEEN YOU AND YOUR GOD.
MMM!
WHAT DOES YOUR GOD SAY?
FOOD
CRISPS!
...IT WAS PRETTY BALLS.

25 DEC 2008

MERRY CHRISTMAS, TOOTS.

26 DEC 2008

BLAH, BLAH, BLAH.
BLAH, BLAH, BLAH, BLAH, BLAH.
BLAH HAHA.
THIS IS THE FIRST TIME I'VE SEEN YOU AND YOUR PARENTS TOGETHER.
OH GOD, YEAH.
I DON'T THINK WE'VE BEEN TOGETHER SINCE THE SPLIT.
OH. WOW.

27 DEC 2008

SHALOM Y'ALL
I STILL LOVE THIS PLAQUE LIA GAVE TO US.
SHADAYIM!
"SHADAYIM"... WHAT DOES THAT MEAN?
BOOBS!

RE: STRANGERS FILM TRAILER

28 DEC 2008

03 JAN 2009

SNIFF SNIFF
POW
HAVE YOU WASHED TODAY?
WHAT? YES!
WHY? DO I SMELL?
NO. YOU JUST DON'T SMELL LIKE WORK OR SOAP.
I DON'T KNOW WHAT IT IS.
DIRT?
SNIFF... NO.
SNIIIIIFF.
HEY!

07 JAN 2009

HMM.
WHAT'S UP?
I PUT MY WORKSHIRT SOMEWHERE AND NOW I CAN'T FIND IT!
PAUSE
IT'S ON YOUR SHOULDER.
!

MAKIN' CHILI
18 JAN 2009
THERE'S SO MUCH HERE!
WE'LL BE ALRIGHT.
THERE'S ENOUGH FOR SIX PEOPLE!
IT'LL BE FINE!
TWO EPISODES OF 30 ROCK LATER...
LEMON!
YOU'RE STILL EATING? IT'S BEEN 45 MINS!
I... I... I CAN'T FEEL MY FACE.

20 JAN 2009

I'M THINKING OF PUTTING ELLERBISMS ON HIATUS.
WHAT? WHY!?
I KEEP FALLING BEHIND ON IT, IT'S STARTING TO BE A STRUGGLE.
BUT IT'S THE BIGGEST THING YOU'RE DOING AT THE MOMENT!
LOOK, JUST REDUCE THE AMOUNT YOU DO FOR A WHILE.
PEOPLE WILL STILL BE HAPPY IT EXISTS RATHER THAN YOU PULLING IT ALTOGETHER.
YEAH. I KNOW. BUT--
MMM. BUT--
NO! C'MON!
YOU CAN'T STOP! IT'S TOO GOOD TO STOP.
OH, OKAY.
GOOD!
NOW STOP BEING SO BLOODY EMO. DINNER'S READY!

TEACHING COMIX @ MAIDSTONE 26 JAN 2009

27 JAN 2009

MISSED THE FAST TRAIN...
D'OH.
LONDON PAPER ON TUBE...
...MISSED THAT, TOO.
Mm.
PHONEZ
O2
YOINK!
MISSED ANNA'S WELCOME.
HEY BABY!
WELL, HER WARM WELCOME, AT LEAST.
HUH?
OH, DON'T WORRY!

28 JAN 2009

YESTERDAY I WAS A TEACHER.
I DON'T KNO
WITH COMICS, IT'S NOT ALWAYS HOW WELL YOU CAN DRAW. IT'S ABOUT HOW WELL YOU TELL THE STORY.
TODAY I'M A BOOKSELLER.
Man
HUFF.
I WONDER WHEN I'LL BE A "COMIC ARTIST" AGAIN?

SNOWDAY 02 FEB 2009

HAVE YOU READ IT, THEN?
YEAH.
IT'S ESSENTIALLY US ISN'T IT?
HERE.
"ARE YOU BREAKING UP WITH ME?"
"I DON'T WANT TO TALK ABOUT IT."
SCOTT PILGRIM
IT'S ME.
NO... NO, IT'S NOT.
WELL... MAYBE A LITTLE.
LATER!
I DON'T GET HOW HE LOVED HER AT FIRST SIGHT, THOUGH. THAT'S ALWAYS BUGGED ME.
WELL, NO, HE TOLD HER HE LOVED HER IN VOLUME 4, BUT HE WAS JUST INTRIGUED BY HER AT THE START, Y'KNOW!
SHE'S THE FIRST GIRL SINCE ENVY TO HAVE THAT SORT OF EFFECT ON H
OHMY GOD, IT IS US!

13 FEB 2009

I COULD EXPLAIN WHY ANNA'S ON THE FLOOR, BUT IT'D TAKE TOO LONG.
MAYBE SHE JUST LIKES HANGING OUT ON THE FLOOR, OKAY?

14 FEB 2009
SO, JUST A LARGE CHIPS, THEN?
NOTHING ELSE?
MMM, UNLESS YOU WANT SOMETHING?
KINDA FANCY A SAVELOY.
OHH, YEAH!
D'YOU WANNA SHARE ONE?
WE CAN GET ONE EACH?
NO, NO IT'S FINE.
OH, IT'S VALENTINE'S DAY AFTER-ALL...
I'LL TREAT YOU.
GEE, THANKS.

TUTORIALS
16 FEB 2009
OKAY. SO. A WEEK TO GO BEFORE HAND IN. WHERE ARE WE AT?
I'VE CHANGED MY IDEA.
I DIDN'T GET 'ROUND TO DOING ANYTHING.
I HAVEN'T DONE MY THUMBNAILS.
SCRIPT? NO?
RIGHT, SO A LITTLE BEHIND THEN?
OHMYGOD YOU ARE ALL SCREWED!

21 FEB 2009

Y'KNOW, I BET THEY STILL LOVE EACH OTHER.
THEY SHOULD'VE BEEN MARRIED BY NOW.
THE SAD THING IS, I WAS GONNA SING AT THEIR WEDDING.
HERO.
BY ENRIQUE IGLESIAS.
I CAN BE YOUR HERO, BABY.

23 FEB 2009

I'LL TEXT YOU WHEN I LAND.
TEXT ME BEFORE.
OK. LOVE YOU BABY.
LOVE YOU!
GULP
CLICK. CLICK. CLICK.
AND SO IT BEGINS.
CLICK. CLICK. CLICK.

24 FEB 2009

25 FEB 2009

26 FEB 2009

HEY YOU.
HEY!
HOW YOU DOIN'?
OH, NOT BAD.
HOW'S YOUR DAY BEEN?
GOOD! WE WENT TO SEE SAGA AND SHE'S ..
HEJ.
HEJ.
I'M JUST ICHATTING TO MARC.
OH, HELLO.
HELLO!
HOW ARE YOU?
FINE, AND YOU?
HEY, I'M CHATTING TO HIM!
IS THAT MARC ON THE ICHAT?
ARGH!
HELLO.

27 FEB 2009

SO, HOW ARE THINGS?
UGH.
THINGS HAVE GOTTEN SO BAD AT WORK, I'VE SPENT THE LAST MONTH SIGNED OFF AND STUCK INDOORS ON THE COUCH AND I HARDLY GET TO SEE MARC
AS TEACHING OR HE'S
D I REALLY DON'T
BACK TO ENGLAND.
AND, I'M STARTING TO REALLY MISS YOU GUYS, TOO.
SIGH.
OH, COME ON!
WOM!

05 MAR 2009

POW!
HEY! WHAT'S WITH YOU?
I'M RESTLESS! I WANT A FIGHT!
YOU WANT A FIGHT?
YEP!
YELP!
I KNOW WHY YOU WANT A FIGHT.
MUH
POW!

06 MAR 2009

WHEN IT COMES TO MARKING WORK I SOMETIMES FEEL A LITTLE OUT OF MY LEAGUE.
IT'S A LITTLE OVERWHELMING AND I FEEL AWFUL GIVING OUT DISMAL GRADES.
BUT YOU HAVE TO DISTANCE YOURSELF FROM IT ALL.
clearly not
42
24/02/09
I'M NOT THEIR FRIEND.
I'M THEIR TUTOR.
ANYTHING LESS WOULD BE UNFAIR TO EVERYONE.

0 7 MAR 2009

THERE ARE 7,000 PENGUINS HERE.
IT'S MID-APRIL, THE MOMENT WHEN THE COUPLES FORM.
WE ARE ASTOUNDED BY THE PARADOX OF THESE DAYS.
THE PENGUINS DEVOTE NEARLY 2 WEEKS TO THEIR MATING "DANCES."
AS IF MOMENTS OF THE HEART CAN'T BE RUSHED.
TWO WEEKS? SOME OTHER CREATURES FROM ICY CLIMATES CAN BE MORE STUBBORN THAN THAT, MATE!

I WANNA STEAL THAT LITTLE DOG.
HUFF
GET YOUR BAG OPEN.
WOW. WE'RE ALL ABOUT THE STEALING AT THE MOMENT.
YEAH. HAHA. WHAT'S IT CALLED? KLEPTOMANIA?
OR IS THAT WHERE YOU SLEEP WITH DEAD PEOPLE?
NO, THAT'S HALEY JOEL OSMENT.
WHU?
THE SIXTH SENSE?
...
NOT "SEES," "SLEEP!"
SLEEPS WITH DEAD PEOPLE!
OH.

CHAPTER FIVE

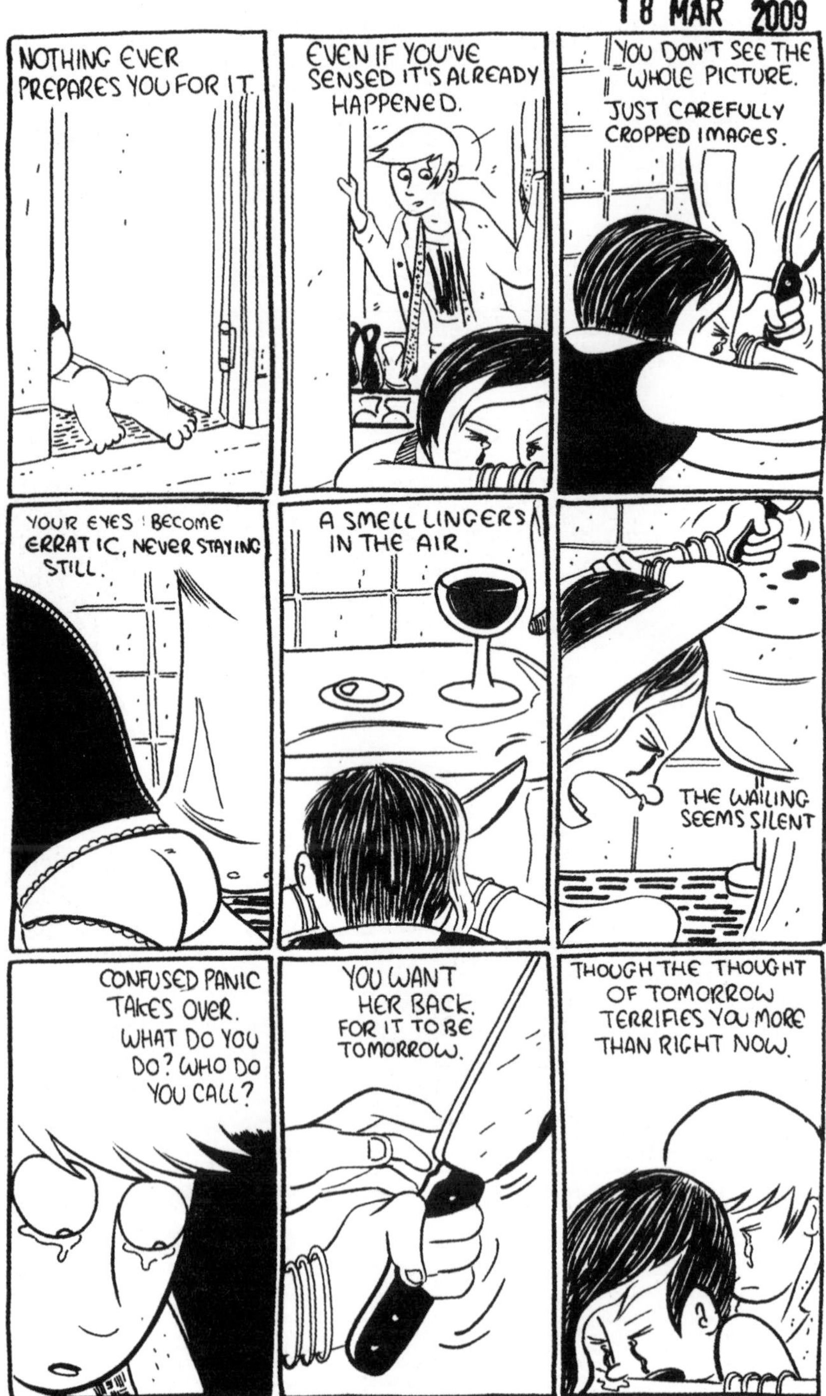
18 MAR 2009
NOTHING EVER PREPARES YOU FOR IT.
EVEN IF YOU'VE SENSED IT'S ALREADY HAPPENED.
YOU DON'T SEE THE WHOLE PICTURE.
JUST CAREFULLY CROPPED IMAGES.
YOUR EYES BECOME ERRATIC, NEVER STAYING STILL.
A SMELL LINGERS IN THE AIR.
THE WAILING SEEMS SILENT
CONFUSED PANIC TAKES OVER.
WHAT DO YOU DO? WHO DO YOU CALL?
YOU WANT HER BACK.
FOR IT TO BE TOMORROW.
THOUGH THE THOUGHT OF TOMORROW TERRIFIES YOU MORE THAN RIGHT NOW.

19 MAR 2009
HEY...
HEY.

20 MAR 2009

WHAT SHIFT ARE YOU DOING TODAY?
12-6 WHAT ARE YOU ON?
MIDDLE. BUT I MIGHT GO IN A BIT EARLIER.
I THINK I'LL SEE IF I CAN~
CHOP CHOP
____BABY?
BABY?
HUH?

23 MAR 2009

I JUST CAN'T GET THAT VISUAL OUT OF MY HEAD.
IT'S LIKE...
...I CAN'T SHAKE IT.
I SEE THAT KNIFE AND THEN I SMELL IT...
I HAD TO WASH THE KNIFE...
...WASH OFF HER --
FUCK.
I KNOW I'VE GOT TO BE THERE FOR HER, BUT I HAVE NO IDEA WHAT I'M DOING, MATT.
WHAT IF SHE DOES IT AGAIN?
I DON'T WANT TO LOSE HER.

27 MAR 2009

'OW LONG'S THIS GONNA TAKE?
ANNA NEEDS BAKING STUFF, SHHH.
HUFFFF.
WELL, I WANT SOME VIMTO!
WHAT THE HELL'S A VIMTO?
IT'S A DRINK, ISN'T IT?
OH, IT'S SO MUCH MORE THAN JUST A DRINK, ANNA.
YOU CAN POUR VIMTO INTO A BOWL OF VANILLA ICE CREAM, MUSH IT UP AND YOU GOT VIMTO FLAVOURED ICE CREAM!
IF YOU'VE GOT A COLD, ADD A SHOT OF DARK RUM TO A MUG OF HOT VIMTO FOR AN EFFECTIVE COLD RELIEF!
VIMTO
OR VIMTOEGAARDEN WHERE YOU MIX A..
IS THIS A NORTHERN THING?
I THINK IT'S A CADWELL THING.
SOAP POW!DER

28 MAR 2009

UGH.
BYE WALLABY!
SEE YA LATER, FOX!
BYEEEE!
11:58
HEY, IT'S NOT THAT LATE.
01:02
WHU?!
OH, FUCK YOU, DAYLIGHT SAVINGS.

GUEST ART BY ADAM CADWELL (OF COURSE)

03 APR 2009

AREN'T YOU NERVOUS ABOUT HAVING YOUR TEETH OUT?
NAH.
BUT THEY'RE TAKING SOME-THING OUT OF YOU.
GOOD!
AND SO
WHAT'S GOING ON, BRUTHA?!
IT'S THE FUZZ! SCARPER!
ENNN!
YOU'LL NEVER TAKE US ALIVE, COPPA!
M M
AFTER THAT...
THERE HE IS.
PTOO
BABY!
LOVE YOU.

06 APR 2009
HEY, WHEN YOU HAD YOUR OPERATION, DID YOU HAVE MAD K.F.C CRAVINGS?
YAHAHAHA. YEAH, WHY, ARE YOU?
OH, GOD, YES! I CAN'T SHUT UP ABOUT IT.
I THINK ANNA'S GETTING SICK OF IT.
I DON'T EVEN LIKE K.F.C!
YAHAHAHA.
YOU HAD A RIGHT GO AT ME FOR HAVING IT AFTER MY OP.
OH, I HAVE A GO AT YOU FOR EVERYTHING.

11 APR 2009

ARE YOU SURE YOU WANNA DO THIS?
YES!
WE'LL HAVE IT AND THAT'LL KILL THE CRAVINGS FOREVER!
KFC
WE HAVE GOT TO STOP THIS OBSESSION!!
A BUCKET?
WHAT ARE WE DOING?
SHHH!
KFC
OHMYGOD, I CAN'T STOOOOP!
POPCORN CHICKEN OM NOM NOM!
L8R...
POP. CORN. CHICK. EN.
UHHHH.
KFC

SWEDEN SPX. PT 1: LOVER'S TIFF 23 APR 2009

LIZZ LUNNEY APPEARS COURTESY OF LIZZLIZZ.COM

SWEDEN SPX PT 2: LUNNEYISMS 24 APR 2009

SWEDEN SPX PT 3: UGH. 25 APR 2009

Toronto Comic Art Festival
01 MAY 2009
WOAH, I CAN'T BELIEVE HOW AWESOME THIS TCAF CON SOUNDS.
TCAF Special
inkstudsradio
1 of 5
0:32
-28:30
MENU
TOMINE, TATSUMI, KATE BEATON, BRY O'MALLEY.
MAN, I WISH I WAS EXHIBITING AT THIS SHOW.
BUT IT'S INVITE-ONLY.
IF ONLY I HAD A PUBLISHER WHO WAS GOING.
OOH, ONI ARE GOING.
HEY! I HAVE A BOOK PUBLISHED BY ONI.
TICK... TOCK... TICK... TOCK.
NOOOO... I COULDN'T.
COULD I?
03 MAY 2009
THANKS STEVE, LOVE TO MUM. YEP. SEE YOU SOON, BYE!
SO, UHHM, WE'VE GOT TWO TICKETS FOR TORONTO.
WE'RE GOING TO TCAF, BABY!

0 6 MAY 2009

HAVE YOU LOOKED AT THE TRAVEL GUIDES, YET?
MMM, YEAH. I FOLDED THE PAGE I WAS LOOKING AT.
THE RESTAURANTS?
HAVE YOU JUST BEEN LOOKING AT WHERE TO EAT?
URRM, YES?
RIGHT. WELL WHAT DID YOU FIND?
OH, I CAN'T REALLY REMEMBER.
I GOT A LITTLE DISTRACTED THINKING ABOUT FOOD SO MUCH I ---
MMM.

07 MAY 2009

ATE 4
TOLIET
ATE4
INTERNATI
DEPARTUR
CUSTOMS
CUSTOM
BAGGAGE RE
rivals
Ar
WE'RE HERE, BABY!
CANADA, TOOTS. WOO!

HEY, DO YOU GUYS WANT TO BE EXTRAS IN A MOVIE?
DEPENDS ON THE MOVIE.
SCOTT PILGRIM VS THE WORLD.
GAAASP!

09 MAY 2009

IF I HAD A RING ON ME. I'D ASK YOU TO MARRY ME.

IF YOU HAD A RING I'D SAY YES.

09 MAY 2009

OKAY SO WE COULDN'T BE IN THE SCOTT PILGRIM MOVIE AS WE'RE NOT CANADIAN NOR DO WE HAVE VISAS.
I KNOW, RIGHT?

BUT THAT DIDN'T STOP US FROM TOTALLY STALKING THE FILMING!
THIS IS WHERE SCOTT PHONES KNIVES!!
IN HIS "DORKY HAT!"
Equipm
TELEPHONE

THE BOYS AT ONI WERE PRETTY MUCH THE BEST PEOPLE EVER AND GOT US "OFFICIALLY" ON SET.
"I HEART THEM SO MUCH."
KNIVES IS PERFECT.
OH YEAH.

WE HAVE MORE MEMORIES OF THAT NIGHT THAN ANY OTHER IN TORONTO.
SCOTT PILGRIM VS THE WORLD

WE QUOTED THE HANDFUL OF LINES WE SAW OVER AND OVER...
"THANK YOU, JULIE."
"THANK YOU JULIE!"

...AND SLEPT LIKE THIS FOR A WEEK...HELL... A MONTH!

TCAF AFTER DRINKS

10 MAY 2009

ROSS CAMPBELL = GREENOBLIVION.COM. JAMIE MCKELVIE = JAMIEMCKELVIE.COM
STEVE LOLSTON = STEVEROLSTON.COM

11 MAY 2009
I REALLY DON'T WANT TO GO HOME...
...I JUST WANT TO STAY RIGHT HERE WITH YOU.

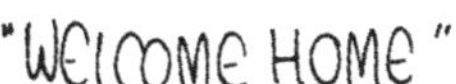

12/13 MAY 2009

LETS JUST TRY AND GET AS MUCH SLEEP AS WE CAN.

OKAY.

LATER

UGH!

WAAA

LATER STILL

BABY. I DON'T FEEL SO GOOD.

UH, OH.

AND SO

RUUARH

LANDED

SHIT, LOOK AT THE RAIN.

iPHONE SAYS IT'S SUNNY IN TORONTO.

LATER, AGAIN.

MAYBE WAIT FOR THE NEXT NEXT ONE?

HOME! (11AM)

LETS GO STRAIGHT TO BED, BABY.

MMM.

FUCKING ENGLAND. UGH!

WE SHOULDN'T HAVE BOTHERED COMING BACK.

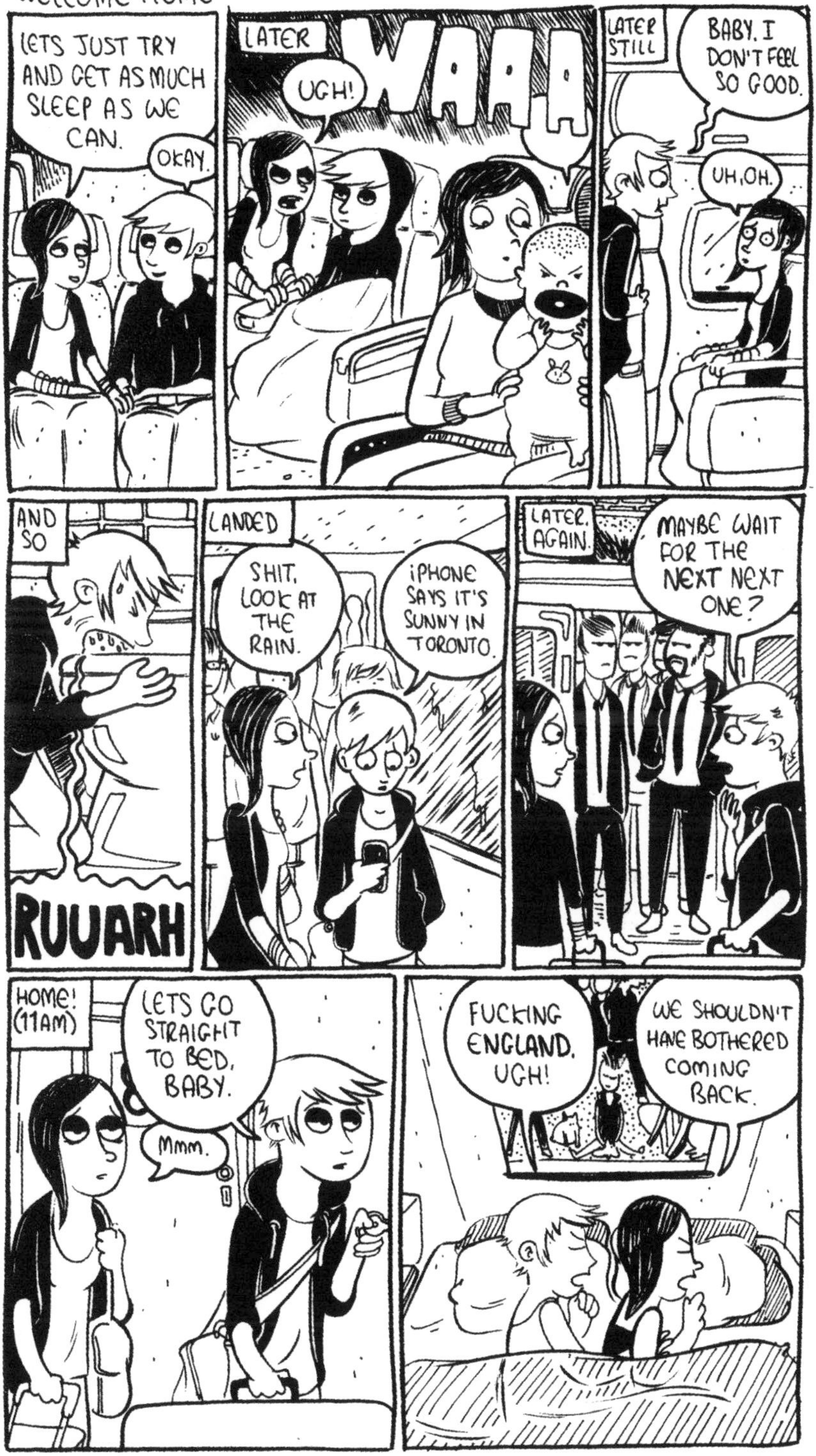

HEY, BABY.
HEY!
MAPLE SYRUP FLAVOURED TEA
Maple Green tea
METRIC-FANTASIES ALBUM
METRIC FANTASIES
MAPLE LEAFS HOCKEY SHIRT
TORONTO MAPLE LEAFS
FREDDIE & ME -BOUGHT AND SIGNED AT TCAF
MISSING CANADA, TOOTS?
WHAT MAKES YOU SAY THAT?

SECOND... THIRD... FOURTH THOUGHTS
04 JUN 2009
WHAT RIGHT DO I HAVE TO DRAW THIS COMIC?
SHE SUPPORTS ME IN IT BUT DOES SHE REALLY WANT THE WORLD TO KNOW ABOUT THIS?
AM I EXPLOITING HER?
SHOULD I NOT PUT IT ONLINE?
MAN, WHAT ARE HER PARENTS GOING TO SAY TO HER?
IS THIS GOING TO SPARK THINGS OFF AGAIN?
WE CAN'T GO THROUGH IT ALL AGAIN.

12 JUN 2009

TAP
TAP
TAP
Z
DING
DING
UGH!
EVERYTHING OKAY, TOOTS?
I COULD'VE SWORN I FAKE-NUMBERED HIM.
WHU?

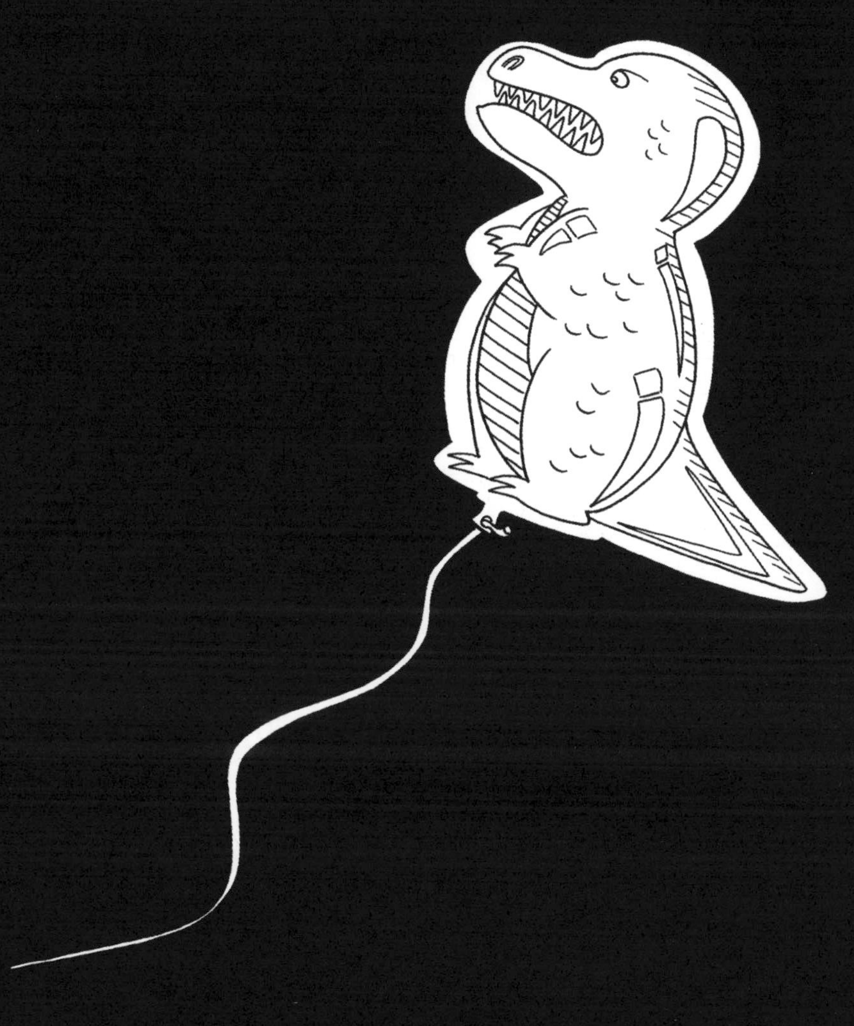

CHAPTER SIX

20 JUN 2009

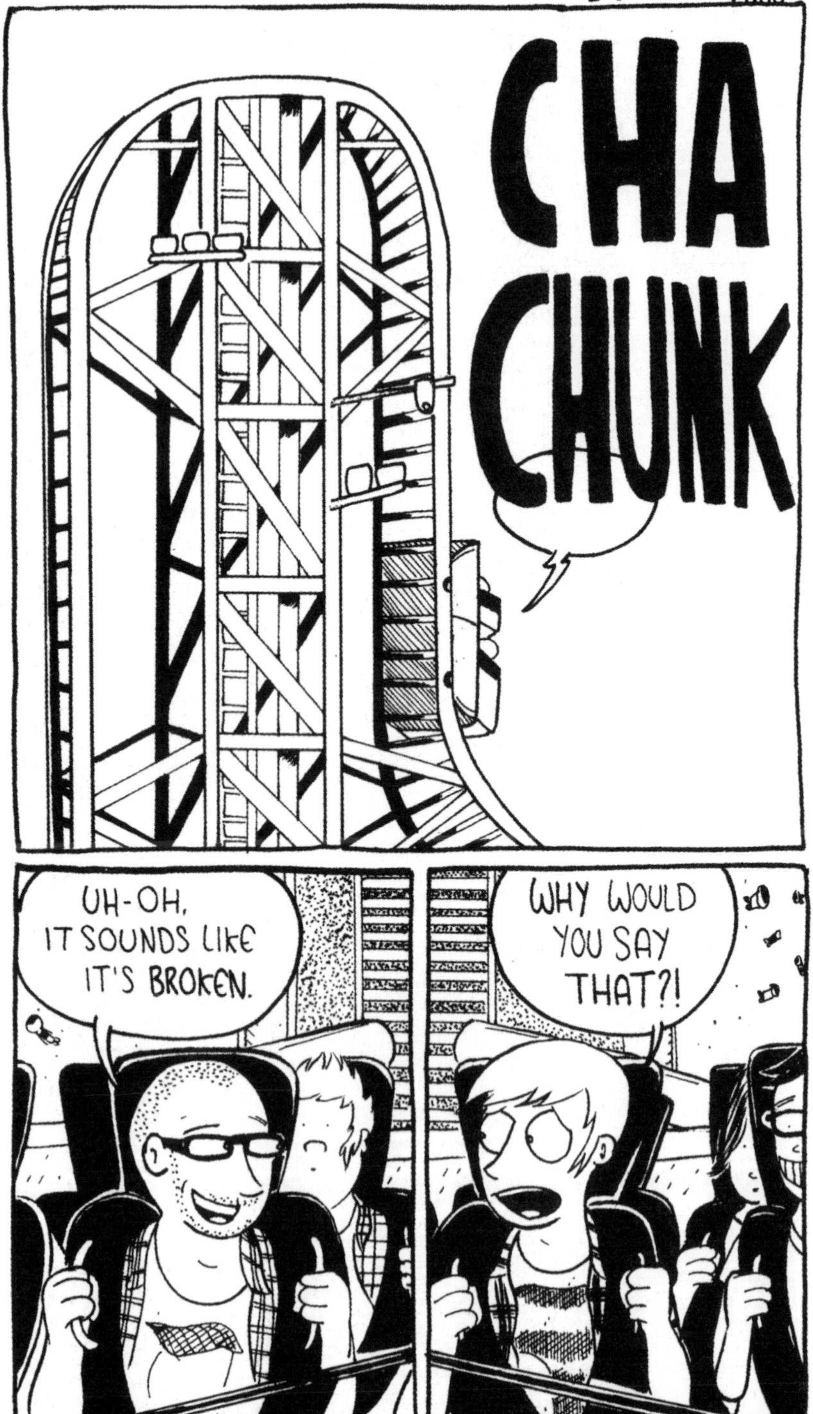

CHA CHUNK

21 JUN 2009

DRACULA, NOOO!

HAPPY BIRTHDAY, TOOTS!

IS THE PAIN GOING UP TO YOUR CHEST?
AAH, YEAH.
YES. SHE'S IN A LOT OF PAIN.
OKAY, I'M DESPATCHING AN AMBULANCE NOW.
THANK YOU.
WHAT HAS SHE EATEN TODAY?
BABY, WHAT HAVE YOU EATEN TODAY?
CEREAL...
AAAH. I HAD BLUEBERRIES FOR LUNCH.
SHE'S HAD BLUEBERRIES.
HMM, IT COULD BE AN ALLERGIC REACTION...
...BUT HOLD THE LINE UNTIL THE AMBULANCE ARRIVES.
OKAY, THANK YOU.
THE AMBULANCE IS COMING, BABY.
I LIKE BLUEBERRIES.
WELL, I'M NOT THEIR BIGGEST FAN, I GOT TO SAY.

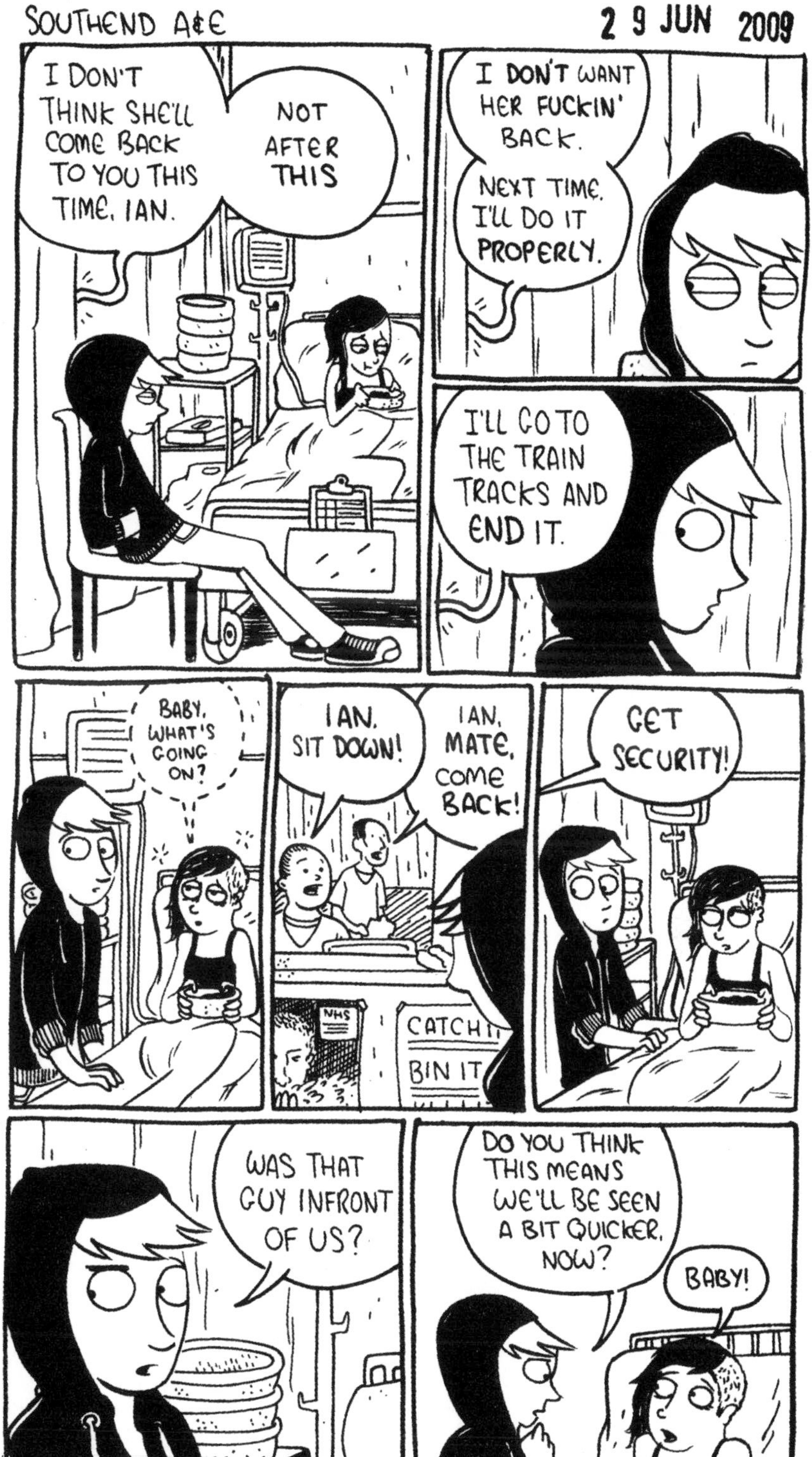

I DON'T THINK SHE'LL COME BACK TO YOU THIS TIME, IAN.

NOT AFTER **THIS**

I **DON'T** WANT HER FUCKIN' BACK.

NEXT TIME, I'LL DO IT **PROPERLY**.

I'LL GO TO THE TRAIN TRACKS AND **END** IT.

BABY, WHAT'S GOING ON?

IAN. SIT **DOWN**!

IAN, MATE, COME BACK!

NHS

CATCH IT

BIN IT

GET SECURITY!

WAS THAT GUY INFRONT OF US?

DO YOU THINK THIS MEANS WE'LL BE SEEN A BIT QUICKER, NOW?

BABY!

1 1 JUL 2009

HOW WAS THE BED LAST NIGHT?
MMM, OKAY.
IT WAS A LITTLE TIGHT.
HMM, IT'S ONLY A 4FT ONE.
WHAT'S YOURS, MUM?
4.6
HMM, NOW THAT'S TOO BIG, YOU SEE?
HMM, IT'S AMAZING WHAT AN EXTRA 6 INCHES CAN DO, THOUGH.
SNORT!
TSK, MARC!

BED TIME FUN TIMEZ

29 JUL 2009

LATER

30 JUL 2009

RUMMAGE.
SNIFFFF.
BLERG!
TOAST IT IS.
SEMI SKIMMED MILK
28-07-0
TWO DAYS LATER
SNIFFFFF
OH! NO!
COK
SOYA
WILL YOU JUST THROW IT AWAY, ALREADY!?

11 AUG 2009

1 2 AUG 2009

KNOWING HOW THE WORLD WORKS IS NOT KNOWING HOW TO WORK THE WORLD.
SLAM
SQUEEEEK
!
SQUEEEEEK
WE DON'T EVEN HAVE A WINDOW CLEANER...

SWEDEN HOLIDAY PT 1
15 AUG 2009
HARRY POTTER
HARRY POTTER
ARE YOU REALLY GOING TO READ HARRY POTTER ALL DAY?
...YES.
HARRY POTTER
RIGHT, WE'RE GOING OUT, THEN.
TO DO WHAT !?!
SWEET.
WOW, THAT WAS SUCH A GOOD IDEA.
TOLD YOU! WHAT SHALL WE DO WHEN WE GET BACK?

SWEDEN HOLIDAY PT 2
16 AUG 2009
HOW WAS ALBIN'S SWIM?
HE WAS A BIT NERVOUS AT FIRST BUT THEN HE LOVED IT.
DEPEC
HA, I THINK HE'S EYEING UP YOUR SANDWICH.
SANDWICHES AREN'T FOR **DOGS**, ALBIN.
WHIIIIIIINE.

SWEDEN HOLIDAY PT3: SPA TIME!

17 AUG 2009

SWEDEN HOLIDAY PT 3

18 AUG 2009

SWEDEN HOLIDAY PT 4 19 AUG 2009

0 9 SEP 2009

WHEN I GET ANNOYED WITH YOU, I WANT TO SCRATCH YOUR EYES.
DO YOU LIKE IT?
FY! FY!

26 SEP 2009

MORE AND MORE RECENTLY I'VE BEEN OBSESSING OVER THE IDEA OF DYING.
LIKE A SMALL ANIMAL DISABLED BY HEADLIGHTS I FREEZE AT THE THOUGHT OF NOT BEING ABLE TO DO ANYTHING.
HOW CAN YOU NOT DO ANYTHING?
HOW CAN YOU NOT FEEL OR TOUCH?
BREATHE? TASTE? THINK?
HOW DO YOU NOT LIVE?
ONE OF US WILL GO BEFORE THE OTHER.
HOW CAN I LIVE WITHOUT HER?
AND NOT JUST FOR A WEEK WHILE SHE VISITS HOME BUT FOREVER.
HOW DO YOU PROCESS THAT?
I'M 26 AND I'M FASTFORWARDING TO THE END.
PONDERING THE INEVITABLE.
LETTING IT GET IN THE WAY OF THE RIGHT NOW.

GASP!
EHH EHH.
BABY. BABY. WHAT'S WRONG?
ENNN, EHHH EHHH.
HEY, HEY. IT'S OKAY.
EHHN.

11 OCT 2009

AFTERWARDS...

EXPO

HEY. DO YOU EVER DANCE TO THE **30 ROCK** THEME TUNE?

OH YEAH! IT'S SO JOLLY.

BAUM BAUM BUH BUDADA BAUM BAUM!
BUH BUDADA BAUM!

DO DO DOODLE DO DO
DO DO DOODLE DO DO

BAUM BAUM BUH BUDADA BAUM BAUM BUH BUDADA BAUM!
BM BM BM BM BM BM BM.

DAH DAH DIDDLE DAH DIDDLE DIDDLE
DAH DAH DUN!

WHAT TOOK YOU GUYS SO LONG?
URRMM.

0 3 NOV 2009

SOMETIMES, I FEEL GUILTY ABOUT BEING IN LOVE WITH ANNA.

SHE'S SO FAR AWAY FROM HER FAMILY AND HER OLD LIFE THAT IT CAN FEEL THAT I'M KEEPING HER FROM THEM.

I DON'T KNOW WHAT IT MUST BE LIKE TO BE SEPARATED FROM SOMETHING THAT MAKES UP SO MUCH OF YOUR IDENTITY.
145 of 176

I'VE ALWAYS ADMIRED HER FOR THAT.
HER STRENGTH CAN BE PRETTY SOLID Y'KNOW?

"IT'S THE SCANDINIVIAN IN HER," I ALWAYS THINK.

I WISH I SAW HIM WHEN I WAS LAST HOME.

ANNA'S GRANDAD DIED TODAY.

I WISH THERE WAS MORE TIME.

I KEEP THINKING THIS PLACE MUST BE THE COMPLETE OPPOSITE OF HER HOME.

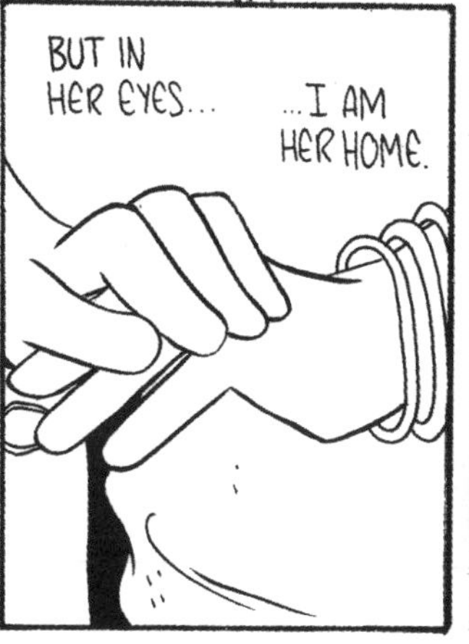
BUT IN HER EYES...
...I AM HER HOME.

LIKE SHE IS MINE.

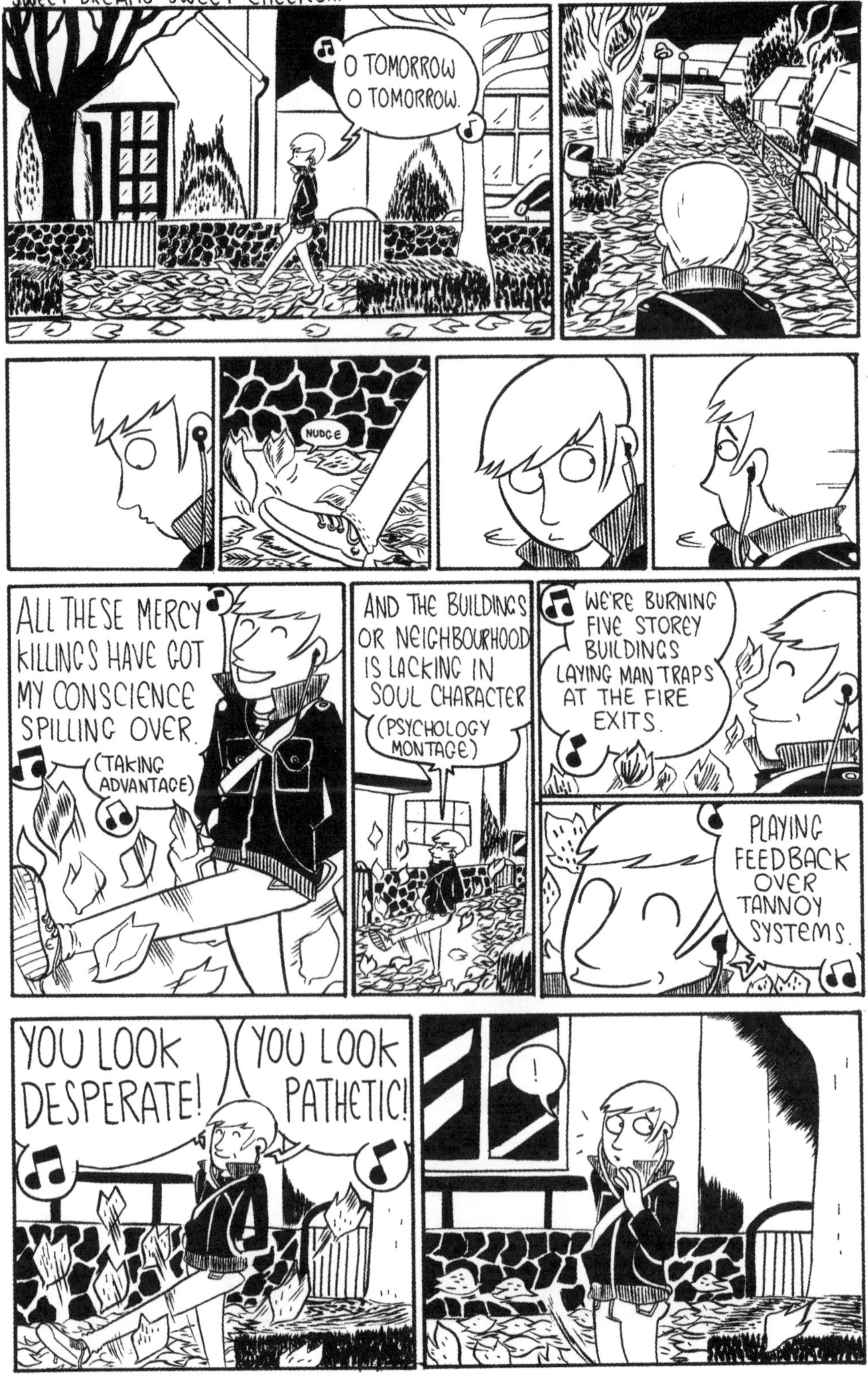

O TOMORROW O TOMORROW.

NUDGE

ALL THESE MERCY KILLINGS HAVE GOT MY CONSCIENCE SPILLING OVER.

(TAKING ADVANTAGE)

AND THE BUILDINGS OR NEIGHBOURHOOD IS LACKING IN SOUL CHARACTER

(PSYCHOLOGY MONTAGE)

WE'RE BURNING FIVE STOREY BUILDINGS LAYING MAN TRAPS AT THE FIRE EXITS.

PLAYING FEEDBACK OVER TANNOY SYSTEMS.

08 NOV 2009
DID YOU HEAR THAT GUY?
NO. WHAT HE SAY?
HE WAS LIKE...
"HOLD ON TRISH. THEY'RE PLAYING THE SMITHS IN 'ERE. I'VE GOTTA GET OUT BEFORE I KILL MESELF."
HA HA.
UGH. I HATE THAT. I REALLY HATE THAT.
WHU?
WHEN PEOPLE SAY THE SMITHS ARE DEPRESSING, I DON'T SEE IT?
IF ANYTHING THE MUSIC IS REALLY UPBEAT.
LIKE "THIS CHARMING MAN."
DIDADIDA DING DING DING A DING DING
THAT'S SUCH A POP RIFF.
IT'S SO HAPPY. IT COULD BE ON SESAME STREET.
THE LYRICS ARE MELANCHOLY, SURE, I'LL GIVE 'EM THAT.
BUT THINK ABOUT WHAT YOU'RE SAYING!?
I WAS IN H&M A WHILE BACK AND THERE WAS THIS LO-FI, FEMALE, ACOUSTIC MUSIC PLAYING.
AND THESE CHAVS ARE LIKE...
..."UGH, THIS IS MAKIN' ME WANNA SLIT MY WRISTS LESSGO."
REALLY? YOU'D RATHER TAKE A BLADE TO YOUR SKIN AND BLEED THAN LISTEN TO A GENRE OF MUSIC?
REALLY?
REALLY, YOU NEANDERTHALS?
HEY, I'M GLAD YOU'VE LEFT, PAL!
I'M GLAD!
I...
...HUH...
WHU?

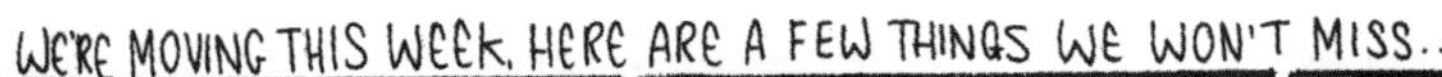
WE'RE MOVING THIS WEEK. HERE ARE A FEW THINGS WE WON'T MISS...

10 NOV 2009

HEEH, I DON'T THINK THIS MANY PEOPLE HAVE EVER FITTED IN THIS FLAT!

WHAT'S ALL THE FUCKIN' NOISE?!

ALRIGHT, CALM DOWN!
YER LIKE A HERDE A FUCKIN' WILDABEASTS. I'M TRYNA SLEEP!

IT'S TWO IN THE AFTERNOON!
HOW ARE WE S'POSED TO KNOW YOU'RE ASLEEP?

SUM OF US WORK SHIFTS, Y'KNOW?

FUCK OFF, WE WORK SHIFTS, TOO.

WE ESPECIALLY WON'T MISS CERTAIN... NOISES.

VRRM
VRRM

ALTHOUGH IT CAN BE CLAUSTROPHOBIC AND WE'VE CERTAINLY OUTGROWN IT...

...THIS WAS OUR FIRST HOME TOGETHER AND WE'LL ALWAYS KINDA LOVE IT...

...IN SOME WEIRD WAY, IT FEELS LIKE WE JUST GOT HERE.

12 NOV 2009

ONE OF THE THINGS THAT WILL ALWAYS STICK IN MY MIND ABOUT THIS PLACE IS THE LADY OPPOSITE US.

WE'VE NEVER REALLY SEEN HER WITH ANYONE.
SHE'LL STAY UP UNTIL THE EARLY HOURS SMOKING AND DOING CROSSWORDS.

I GOT IT IN MY HEAD THAT SHE WAS LONELY BECAUSE SHE WAS ALONE.

THE FIRST TIME I SAW HER I COULD'VE SWORN SHE WAS MY MUM.

SAME HAIR.
SAME BUILD.
SAME HEIGHT.

THAT'S PROBABLY WHAT SPARKED OFF MY WORRY TO BE HONEST.

NOW AND AGAIN I'D HEAR HER PHONE RING AND I HOPED IT WAS A SON OR DAUGHTER.

RING
RING
RING
RING

NO ONE SHOULD BE TRULY ALONE.
RING

I HOPE I'M WRONG.
I HOPE SHE'S THE HAPPIEST STRANGER I'LL NEVER MEET.

MOVING
14 NOV 2009
THIS IS A SIGN!
I'M TELLING YOU. THIS IS A SIGN WE SHOULDN'T BE MOVING!
BED
IF YOU GUYS MOVE AGAIN, GET A TRUCK.
ONE TRIP! DONE! BAM!
BAH.
RIGHT, WE'RE GOING TO GET ANOTHER LOT.
ARE YOU GOING TO COME WITH TO HELP?
BED
TBS
KITCHEN
HMM. NO.
NO, I'M GOING TO STAY AND UNPACK.
...
BED
TBS
KITCHEN
RIGHT. OKAY.
MAN. I WISH I HAD THOUGHT OF THAT.

THERE!
THIS TAPE OUGHTA KEEP A BIT OF THE COLD OUT.
I'LL TEXT THE LANDLORDS, SEE IF THEY KNOW HOW TO FIX THE GAP.
KAY.
URRM.
OOH.
URRMMM.
ANNA!
ANNNAAA!
I CAN'T GET DOWN.
RRRRIGHT.
OOF.
THANKS TOOTS.

24 DEC 2009

AWW!

LOOK HOW CUTE HE IS!

THANKS, BABY!

YOU CAN OPEN THIS ONE.
KAY!

RRRIIIIIIP.

EEEEEEE!

LOOK AT THEIR LITTLE FACES!
WEST HIGHLAND WHITE TERRIERS
2010 CAL

THANKS TOOTS!
BABY!

CHAPTER SEVEN

LETS HAVE A LOOK AT YOUR NEW SPECS THEN, MARC-BOY.
OKAY.

I WAS GOING TO GET THE ONES ANNA HAS BUT THESE FITTED MY FACE BETTER.

...I LIKE 'EM BUT I THINK THE OTHERS WOULD SUIT YOU BETTER...
...THEY'RE MORE WEEZER-ISH.
SLURP.

GOOD ONE KEV!!
WHU?

I WANNA BE WEEZER.
UGH.
WHOOPS...

16 JAN 2010

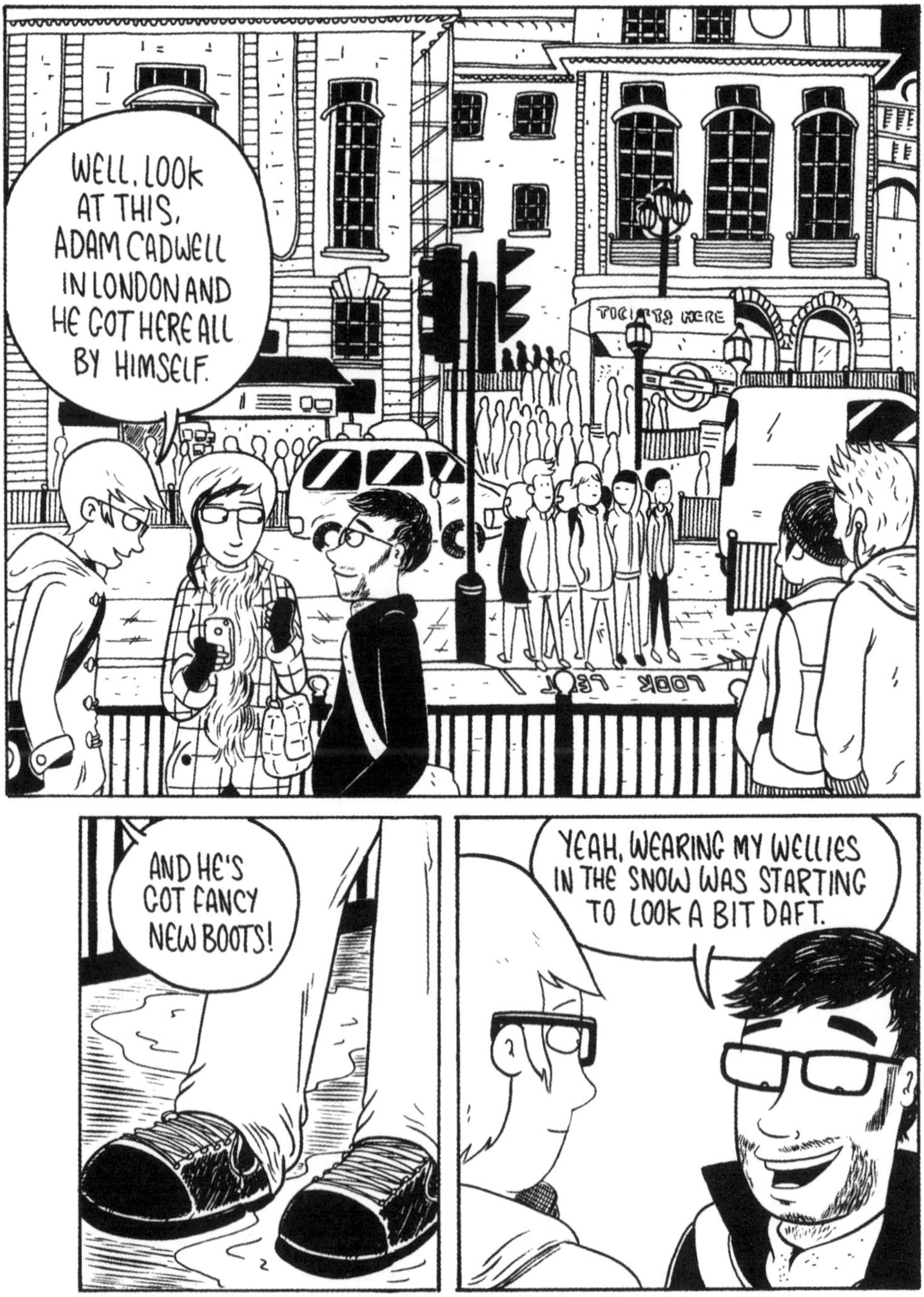

WELL, LOOK AT THIS, ADAM CADWELL IN LONDON AND HE GOT HERE ALL BY HIMSELF.

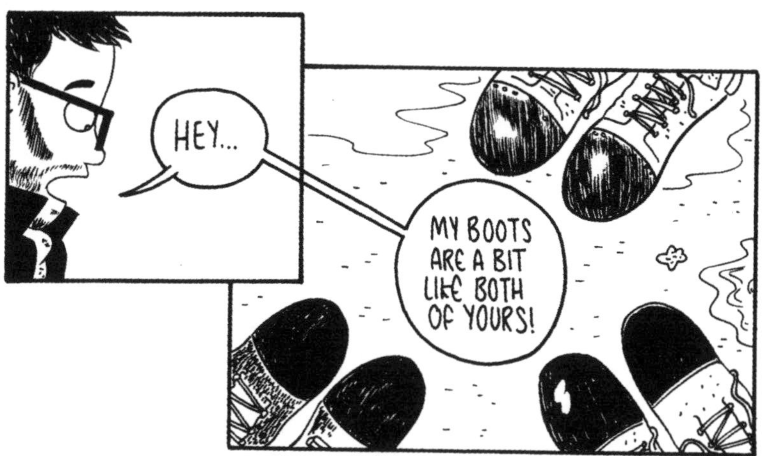
HEY...
MY BOOTS ARE A BIT LIKE BOTH OF YOURS!

AND YOU'VE BOTH GOT NEW GLASSES LIKE MINE!

YOU GUYS TRYING TO LOOK LIKE ME?

WE'RE CADWELL COSPLAYING!
LETS ORDER THE SAME THING AT DINNER!
I ♡ LDN

19 JAN 2010

SLURPY.

SOMETHING'S HAPPENING, DON'T SPEAK TOO SOON.

I TOLD THE BOSS AND MADE MOVE
IS THAT ELLIOTT SMITH PLAYING?
OH, NO...
DUNNO WHERE TO GO.
SON OF SAM, SON OF A

...I'VE BECOME AN INDIE COMIC PARODY...
BLACK RIMMED GLASSES
WEARING A SCARF INDOORS
DRAWING AUTOBIO COMICS
DRINKING BLACK COFFEE
CARDIGAN!

I GOTTA GET OUT OF HERE!

WOOOAAA

YEAH, THAT GUY'S SO GAY.
TOTALLY.

06 FEB 2010

HAS ADAM DRAWN YOU IN 'THE EVERYDAY' YET, KAYLA?
ERRM. I'M IN MONDAY'S STRIP, RIGHT?
YUP.
SNIGGER.
SNIGGER.
SNIGGER.
WHAT? WHAT?
OH IT'S JUST, Y'KNOW, CADWELL KISSES A GIRL... THEY USUALLY END UP IN A COMIC.
OH. I'VE HEARD ABOUT THIS...
HA. IN ISSUE 2 THERE WAS LIKE ONE A PAGE OR SOMETHING!
WELL, I'M REALLY GLAD YOU'VE BROUGHT THIS UP.
HAHA, SORRY!
I'M GONNA GET THAT ISSUE.
HUH?

06 FEB 2010

WOA
HOHO
HOHO

IF YOU LIKE IT THEN YOU SHOULDA PUT A RING ON IT
IF YOU LIKE IT THEN YOU SHOULDA PUT A RING ON IT

IF YOU LIKE THINGS PUT RINGS ON 'EM!
IF YOU LIKE RINGS, PUT RINGS ON THINGS!

"ARE YOU ON THE NEXT TRAIN?"
19:12
TAP TYPE TAP
BONG
PLATFORM FOUR FOR THE 19.15 SERVICE TO SHOEBURYNESS.
!
POKE
O2-UK 3G 19:14
Anna
Mum
Jim
Matty Voi
"YOU HAVE REACHED THE O2 MESSAGING SERV_ _
IS YOUR PHONE DEAD?
NO?
OH, I JUST GOT A TEXT FROM YOU.
BEEP
MMM, I ALSO RANG. YOU COULD'VE LET ME KNOW WHAT TRAIN YOU WERE...
BEEP BEEP.
...ON.
Anna
I am here!
Close
Reply

WHY IS IT SO HOT ALL OF A SUDDEN?
LIKE... IT'S KINDA... KINDA...
WHAT THE HELL?
WHAT'S WRONG WITH ME?
NEED TO GET OUT OF HERE.
SHIT. JUST CHAVS FOR HELP.
JUST GET TO THE NEXT STOP.
JUST... JUST... GET... ANNA... I NEED ANNA.

AND SO...
rrock University Hospitals NHS
rsity Hospital

MARC ELLDERBY!
CRUM BLE.
TSK.
TAKE THE
MY TURN!
OW LONG
CKIN NHS
YOU'RE UP.
YEAH.

OKAY. WHAT'S THE PROBLEM?
I LOST MY, URM, VISION ON THE TRAIN AND CAME OVER ALL HOT...
NO
FLU

THAT AND, URRM, MY DOWNSTAIRS HAVE BEEN HURTING FOR A DAY OR TWO...

...
RIGHT. LETS TAKE A LOOK, THEN.

WELL, IT LOOKS OKAY TO ME.

A WHILE LATER...
NOTHING STANDS OUT AS BEING WRONG AND I'M NOT GOING TO INVEST MY TIME TO FIND OUT.
HERE'S A PRESCRIPTION.

WELL HOPEFULLY THESE DRUGS WILL HELP.
MMM.

TWO DAYS LATER...
WRUG!

CUST
I'LL SEE YOU ON THE OTHER SIDE
OKAY, TOOTS.
HEJ.
HEJ.
TACK.
...TACK.
WHAT THE?
YOUR COUNTRY'S TOO LIBERAL!
omme

14 MAR 2010

BABY...
...HOW ARE YOU FEELING?
I'M DYING.
YOU'RE NOT DYING.
ARE YOU SURE?
ALWAYS, BABY.

CONTINUES USED 11
THIS GAME HAS BEEN TAUNTING ME FOR 20 YEARS.

IT SHOULDN'T EVEN BE THIS HARD. THERE'S ONLY 2 BUTTONS

FORWARDS.
JUMP.

I WAS PLAYING IT EARLIER AND I DIED SO MANY TIMES A MESSAGE CAME UP ASKING IF I'D LIKE A "WALK-THROUGH."
HAHA!

I DON'T LIKE IT BECAUSE I CAN'T BLOWUP ANYONE.

DLING
WELL THERE IS THAT TO IT, I GUESS...

FRO

FRO

ARF!

ARF!
ARF!

...
...
...
HUH?

OKAY GUYS, SETTLE DOWN!
ICONOGRAPHY
IMAGES
PANELS
SPEECH
RIGHT GUYS, THIS IS MARC, HE'S A COMICS ILLUSTRATOR AND HE'S HERE TO HELP YOU WITH YOUR COMIC STRIPS.
HI!
SO, I JUST WANNA QUICKLY SHOW YOU GUYS SOME OF MY DRAWINGS ON THE SCREEN...
WOW!
ARE YOU FAMOUS?!
AM I FAMOUS!?
NO.
NO, I'M REALLY NOT.

WITH MY... UMM... DOWNSTAIRS STILL BEING A COMPLETE SHIT AND MY G.P HAVING NO REAL IDEAS...
I'LL SEND YOU FOR ANOTHER BLOOD TEST BUT, HMM. I'M NOT THAT SURE WHAT'S WRONG.

...I DECIDED TO CUT MY LOSSES AND TRY A SEXUAL HEALTH CLINIC, INSTEAD.
2
3

THESE CLINICS AREN'T SO BAD, REALLY, JUST A LITTLE AWKWARD IN PLACES.
DUM DE DUM.

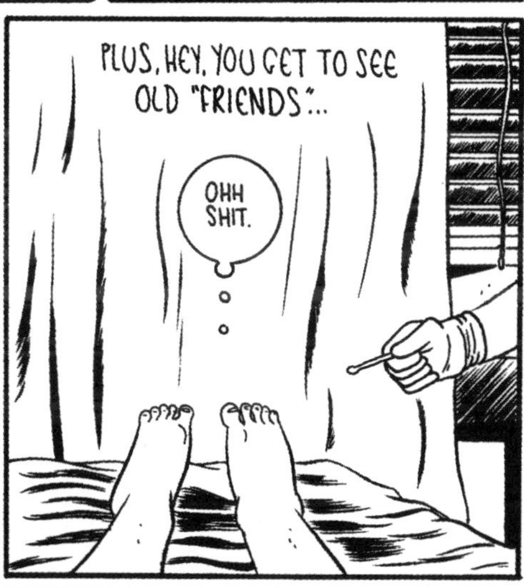
PLUS, HEY, YOU GET TO SEE OLD "FRIENDS"...
OHH SHIT.

ANYWAY, THE DOC WHO FINALLY SAW ME WAS A LITTLE... ERRATIC, SHALL WE SAY.
NOW, WE HAVE MARC, WITH A C WHO IS YOU. WITH A C. LIKE MARC BOLAN.
PEN! I NEED A PEN!

HE REMINDED ME A BIT OF A MIX OF DAVID FROST AND DOC BROWN (NOT THE MENTAL IMAGE YOU WANT WHILE SOMEONE POKES AROUND DOWN THERE...)
GREAT SCOTT.

HE ALSO KEPT SAYING...
I AM DR. EVANS. THAT'S EVANS WITH AN A.
TRADITIONAL WELSH NAME.

WHICH CONFUSED ME AS I DIDN'T REALISE THERE WAS ANOTHER SPELLING.
WHAT DOES THIS HAVE TO DO WITH MY BITS?

I AM 95% SURE YOU'VE GOT PROSTATITIS 95.9% SURE.
IT'S NOT TH--

AND THE SECOND HE MENTIONED MY PROSTATE THERE WAS ONLY ONE WORD THAT CAME CRASHING DOWN.
CANCER
BECAUSE, WELL, IT WOULD, WOULDN'T IT?

AND SO I NODDED ALONG WITH WHATEVER HE SAID FOR HOWEVER LONG WHILE THINKING ABOUT ANNA AND THE FUTURE, HOPES, DREAMS...

...AND I'M PRETTY MUCH WRITING OFF MY LIFE...

IT DOESN'T POINT TO CANCER, SO WE'LL LET YOU KNOW THE RESULTS.

...AAAND WE'RE BACK IN THE ROOM.

FOR THAT SECOND WHERE YOU THINK THE END HAS BEEN WRITTEN YOU REALISE HOW MUCH YOU WANT TO KEEP WHAT YOU ALREADY HAVE.

AND YOU THINK ABOUT THE THINGS THAT BRING YOU DOWN, LIKE THE JOB YOU DESPISE AND THIS VERY COMIC.
HONESTLY. SHOULD I BE TELLING YOU ANY OF THIS?

THIS IS MY LIFE AND I LIKE IT A WHOLE BUNCH.
MAYBE IT'S TIME I RECLAIMED IT.

Thorpe Park
MY FAKE MOUSTACHE WON'T STAY ON!
YOU GOTTA HOLD IT WITH YOUR TOP LIP.

FEE!

AND THEN YOU HAVE TO FALK LIKE A FUNDERFIRD FUFFET.

A WHAT?
A FUNDERFIRD FUFFET!!!

LATER...

AAAAAAAAAAA
I'M NOT GOING ON THAT...

COME ON MAN. WHY NOT?

UPSIDE DOWN MAKES ME VOMIT.

THE KEG, TORONTO

0 4 MAY 2010

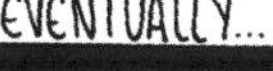

TSSSSHHH
WOW ...

...THAT'S A LOT OF WATER.
HA!
MAID

BABY, ISN'T THIS THE MOST BEAUTIFUL SIGHT YOU'VE EVER SEEN?

ONE OF THE MOST BEAUTIFUL SIGHTS, TOOTS.
CLICK

YUCK!

WELL I'VE GOT STYLE...

...MILES AND MILES...

...SO MUCH STYLE THAT IT'S WASTING ...

...SO MUCH STYLE THAT IT'S WASTING ...

SO MUCH STYLE THA
WILL YOU SING THE REST OF THE SONG ALREADY !!!

I CAN'T REMEMBER THE REST.

THEN STOP SINGING IT THEN!?

QUEEN

SO MUCH STYLE THAT IT'S WASTING!
GRR!

PERILS OF AUTOBIOGRAPHY PANEL @ TCAF

08 MAY 2010

CASA LOMA
10 MAY 2010

Y'KNOW, THIS IS WHERE THEY FILMED X-MEN!
GASP! XAVIER'S SCHOOL FOR GIFTED YOUNGSTERS!

THIS IS THE BIT WHERE THEY BURY JEAN IN X-MEN 3.

THAT'S WHERE WOLVIE LEAPS AT STRYKER'S MEN IN X2.
CLICK

THIS CORRIDOR IS WHERE THE YOUNG MUTANTS HIDE.
WITH THE SECRET PASSAGE !?

YOU GOTTA SEE WHAT I'VE JUST FOUND.

YOU KNOW WHO THESE BELONG TO, RIGHT?

YAH-UH!
GET A PHOTO OF ME WITH THEM!

I WANT TO SHOW YOU SOMETHING!
OK!
GASP!
THE T.A.R.D.I.S!!
POLICE BOX
WHAT?
NO, LOOK!
IT'S A BABY?
AND LOOK HOW CUTE SHE IS.
WELL, IT'S NO T.A.R.D.I.S. AND_ _
DAWW!

SCRIBBLE
FWIP

TSK.
EDTLER
Plastic

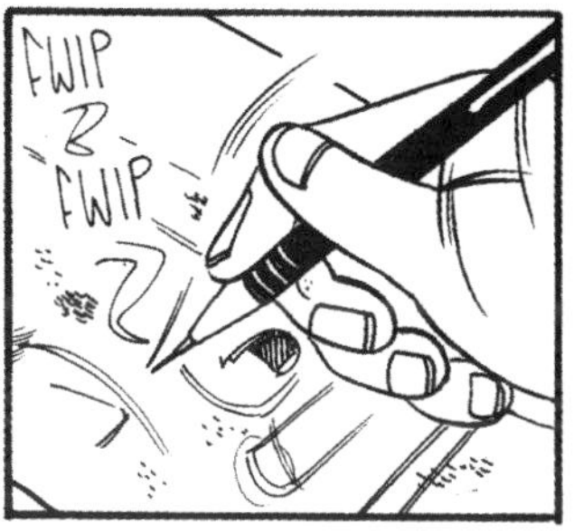
FWIP
FWIP

ENN
ENN

CLICK
CLICK

TSK!
SCRRTCH

ENN
ENN

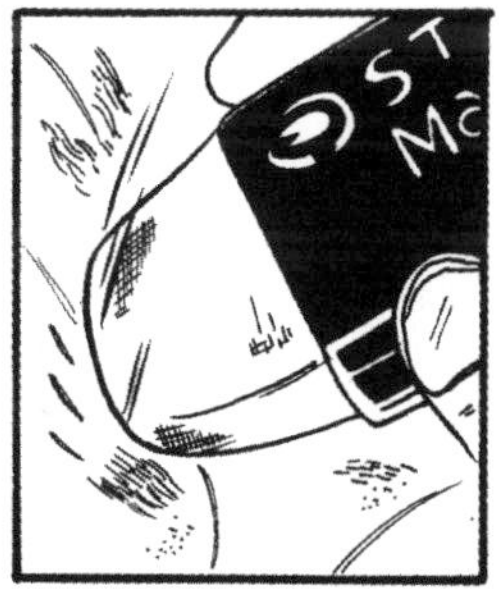

FUCKING!
BOM

RAA!

STUPID!
FUCKING!
COMIC!
WOMP
RING
RING
RING
RING
02-Uk 3G
Toots
mobile
...HI.
HEY.
WHAT ARE YOU UP TO?
...I'M...
...I'M NOT DOING SO GREAT.

MUM BLE.
MUM BLE.
HA HA!

BOOM!
MUM BLE.
HA HA HA!
MUM BLE.
KRASH
WHU!?

MUM BLE.
HAHAHA!
BANG!
MUM BLE.

MUM BLE.
MUM BLE.
STOM
HAHABANG
MUM BLE.

FUCKING ARSE HOLES!
AHH HHH!

HEY!
MUM BLE
MUM BLE
BABY. WHAT'S WRONG..

SHUT THE FUCK UP WE'RE TRYNA FUCKING SLEEP DOWN HERE!
MUM BLE
MUM BLE
BOOM

MUM BLE
MUM BLE
MUM BLE

WHAT IS GOING ON WITH YOU?

MINE AND MATT'S PHONE CALLS ALWAYS HAVE THESE LONG PAUSES IN THEM.
HELLO ...
... HI ...
...WHAT YOU DOING? ...
... JUST WATCHING T.V...
... "I HAVE TO GO NOW" ...
WHO ARE YOU ON THE PHONE TO?
...I WAS CARRYING ON YOUR JOKE.
OH, I THOUGHT YOU WERE TWEETING.
RIGHT. YEAH I WAS TALKING TO TWITTER ...
HELLO, TWITTER?
YES, I'D LIKE TO MAKE A TWEET, PLEASE.
WOW! CAN YOU DO THAT?
...NO, THIS IS ALSO A JOKE.

WELL IT'S A SHAME ANNA COULDN'T BE HERE.
I WAS SAYING TO YOUR MOTHER, WE LOVE IT WHEN YOU COME OVER.
WHY ISN'T SHE HERE?
DING!
SHE'S GETTING A TATTOO.
OH, I THOUGHT SHE MIGHT BE AT WORK.
IT'S SO BIG...
HAS SHE SENT YOU A PICTURE?
LET'S HAVE A LOOK.
BLOODY HECK, LAD!
DIDN'T YOU KNOW HOW BIG SHE WAS GETTING IT?
SHE...
...SHE DIDN'T SAY SHE WAS GETTING IT THAT BIG...

...IT'S JUST A BIT SHOCKING.

SHOCKING?
WELL, YEAH. IT'S HUGE.

IT'S A BACKPIECE OF COURSE IT'S GOING TO BE BIG.
ANY SMALLER AND YOU WON'T SEE THE DETAIL.

BUT YOU SAID IT WASN'T GOING TO BE THAT BIG!

WELL, I KNEW YOU'D FREAK OUT AND TRY AND CHANGE MY MIND AND I REALLY WANTED IT.
I'VE WANTED IT FOR SO LONG.

BUT I'M THE ONE WHO HAS TO LOOK AT IT.

'HAS' TO LOOK AT IT?

I DIDN'T SPEND 6 HOURS IN AGONY FOR YOU TO BE A DICK.
THAT'S..
NO! YOU UNSUPPORTIVE SHIT, I'VE JUST HAD IT DONE!

BABY..
FUCKING LEAVE ME ALONE.

THE END PT 3.

I DON'T KNOW WHAT TO SAY, MARC.

DO YOU THINK DAD WOULD PUT ME UP?

JUST TALK TO HER FIRST AND DON'T RUSH INTO ANYTHING.

SHE SAID IT WOULDN'T BE THAT BIG.

YOU THINK SHE WAS PERFECT THE WAY SHE WAS?
YEAH.

WELL SHE OBVIOUSLY THOUGHT ABOUT IT.
SHE'S STILL ANNA.

IT'S NOT LIKE SHE LOST A LEG.
EXACTLY.

I DON'T EVEN KNOW IF IT'S THE TATTOO I'M WORKED UP OVER.

I HAVEN'T FELT OKAY IN A WHILE...
...EVERYTHING'S STARTING TO GET TO ME.

CLICK.

HI.

HEY.

I'M SORRY FOR BEING A NOB.

13 JUN 2010

YOU CAN NAME THE DRAGON IF YOU WANT.

DOES THAT MEAN YOU'VE NAMED THE TIGER?
MAJA!

THAT'S NOT MAJA!
FY MAJA!

FY.
FY.

I LOVE YOU.
LOVE YOU, TOO.

EPILOGUE

2 1 APR 2011
STEV
SELF HIRE
I RECKON I'LL BE OFF THEN.
WELL THANKS FOR HELPING OUT.
NIRVANA
DVD'S
THANKS FOR PAYING ME. I'LL BE IN TOUCH LATER.
COOL, MAN. TAKE IT EASY.
LATERS.

I AM NOT LOOKING FORWARD TO UNPACKING ANY OF THIS.
AND YOU WON'T HELP WILL YOU, ALICE-WALICE?
'OW!
NO, NO YOU WON'T.
SLUP
I LOVE YOU...
NIRVA
NIRVANA
BOOK
LIVING
BO
DON'T.
PLEASE DON'T MAKE THIS HARDER THAN IT HAS TO BE.

'OW.
SORRY.
I MEAN, I LOVE YOU...
...GEORGE.
HEH.
I'M GOING TO MAKE A MOVE, I THINK.
YEAH?
YEAH, YOU'VE GOT LOADS OF STUFF TO DO.
I GUESS.

LET ME KNOW ABOUT GETTING THE OLD PLACE SORTED.
SURE. I'LL TEXT JAMES TO SEE WHEN HE WANTS HIS KEYS BACK.
ALRIGHT. WELL TEXT ME IF YOU NEED ANYTHING.
NIRVANA
YOU BE A GOOD GIRL FOR MUMMY, ALICE.
YOU TOO, LITTLE MAN.
I MISS THEM SO MUCH.

I'LL TEXT YOU.
OKAY, WELL ...
BYE.

18
17
CLICK
IT'S HARD TO PINPOINT WHERE EXACTLY IT WENT WRONG FOR US.
I HAVEN'T SUBCONSCIOUSLY BLOCKED IT FROM MY MIND OR ANYTHING LIKE THAT.
IT'S JUST OUR BREAK-UP WASN'T **ONE** LIFE-SHATTERING EVENT.
MORE "A BLOCK OF TIME" FILLED WITH NON-EVENTS WHERE THE TWO OF US JUST STOPPED BEING A COUPLE.
IRVA
AND SO IN TURN STOPPED BEING **TOGETHER.**

WITHOUT EVEN NOTICING WE WERE DOING IT, WE **PRIORITIZED** EVERYTHING ELSE ABOVE OUR RELATIONSHIP AND TOOK OUR LOVE FOR GRANTED.
I'M OFF, BABY.
WE WERE IN **LOVE**, SURE. BUT WE WEREN'T **LOVERS** ANYMORE.

WE STARTED TO DECLARE LOVE ALMOST OUT OF HABIT.
"I LOVE YOU."

"I LOVE YOU, TOO."

AND ALTHOUGH WE MEANT IT, WE HAD STOPPED SHOWING IT. THERE WAS NO **BACKBONE** IN THOSE THREE LITTLE WORDS, ANYMORE.

THERE WAS NO PROOF OF OUR SENTIMENTS.

OUR LIFE BECAME THIS SCHEDULE THAT BARELY SYNCHED.

HER WORK HOURS VS. MY WORK HOURS VS. HER GYM TIME VS. MY DRAWING TIME, COMMITMENTS TO THIS, THAT, THE OTHER.

WHEN WE DID GET TO SPEND TIME TOGETHER IT WAS LIKE WE WEREN'T REALLY THERE.

WE WERE SO EXHAUSTED FROM DOING EVERYTHING ELSE.
HI.
HI.

OR MAYBE WE WEREN'T REALLY IN TO IT.

OR, WHATEVER...

WE GOT TWO LITTLE ADDITIONS TO OUR FAMILY. (IN HINDSIGHT TO FILL A VOID WE WERE BOTH GUILTY OF CREATING.)

TWO PERFECT KITTIES; GEORGE THE CONFIDENT, ATTENTION-SEEKING LITTLE MAN.
ALICE!

AND ALICE, THE SHY, RESERVED FEMALE.
ALRIGHT, THERE YOU GO.

WE LOVED THEM INSTANTLY.
HOW COULD YOU NOT?

WE PUSHED OUR TROUBLES TO ONE SIDE, IGNORING WHAT WAS STARING AT US.
BEEP

BOTH TRYING HARD TO HOLD ON...
TAP TAP

... BUT DELAYING THE INEVITABLE.
13.12
Toots
Edit
Messages
I don't know. I think there's so much we need to talk about that we've been needing to talk about for awhile. I guess it's kinda obvious I'm not happy? x
Send

SHIT.
I THINK ANNA'S GOING TO DUMP ME.

WHAT?!
SINCE WHEN?

IT'S PROBABLY LONG OVER-DUE, MAN.

THE ROOM FEELS LIKE A PRISON. I CAN SMELL THE CIGARETTES SHE'S NERVOUSLY DEVOURED AND I JUST WANT TO ESCAPE.
I KNOW THE LAST FEW WEEKS HAVEN'T BEEN EASY.

I REVERTED BACK TO A SCHOOL BOY, LOOKING AT THE FLOOR, AT MY HANDS TRYING TO AVOID WHAT WAS COMING.

...BUT I'M SO UNHAPPY AND I KNOW YOU ARE, TOO.
WITH ME, WITH THIS PLACE.

I CAN GIVE US SOME ROOM...
...I CAN. WE S-SHOULD FIGURE OUT WHAT WE WANT.
THAT CAME OUT ALMOST TOO EASY.

WHEN DID IT GO ALL SO WRONG?

IT'S A QUESTION NEITHER OF US CAN ANSWER.

I MOVED IN WITH MY FRIEND DAVE FOR WHAT WAS SUPPOSE TO BE A WEEK.
HEY.

"IT'LL ALL BE SORTED SOON, ME AND ANNA WILL WORK IT OUT."
DRINK?
GOD, YES.

WHO WAS I TRYING TO FOOL?

AND SO FOR THE FIRST TIME IN A WHILE IT FELT LIKE I DIDN'T HAVE A HOME.
NIGHT, MAN.
SEE YOU TOMORROW.

DAVE'S BIG INTO AMERICAN FOOTBALL SO TROPHIES SIT PROUDLY ON THE BEDSIDE AND HEROES ADORN THE WALLS OF THE ROOM I'M STAYING IN.

THE IRONY ISN'T LOST ON ME.

I WANTED TO GIVE US ANOTHER SHOT TRULY BELIEVING WE WERE RIGHT FOR ONE ANOTHER...
I WANT TO GET MY OWN PLACE.
I WANT TO LIVE ON MY OWN.

I DIDN'T WANT TO LET HER GO...
SO WE'RE ...WE'RE DONE THEN?

SHIT...

BUT THEN THIS WASN'T JUST ABOUT WHAT I WANTED.
HEY
HEY. I'M SORRY.

AND I COULDN'T DENY IT ANY LONGER.
THIS IS HARD FOR ME TOO.

HEY, C'MON, LETS GET GOING.

THERE'S SO MUCH TO SAY BUT DEEP DOWN I KNOW IT WON'T DO ANYTHING.

THIS IS WHAT SHE WANTS, WHAT SHE NEEDS.

ANNA HAS THIS BOOMING LAUGH THAT CONTROLS THE ROOM. IT'S ONE OF MY FAVOURITE THINGS ABOUT HER.
HA!

I HAVEN'T HEARD THAT LAUGH FOR SO LONG.

SO I REALISE, WHO AM I TO DENY HER HAPPINESS?

AGE
BONMARCHE
ANNA IS A BEAUTIFUL, LOVING WOMAN AND I KNOW SHE'LL BE HAPPY AGAIN.

MAYBE IT'S SELFISH TO SAY BUT IT'S CRUSHING TO KNOW I WON'T SEE IT HAPPEN.
AGE

AND SO WITH ALL BREAK-UPS, YOU REMEMBER THE START.
YEARN FOR THE GOOD TIMES.

TRICKING YOURSELF THAT IT WILL BE OKAY. YOU WILL SEE HER FACE IN THE MORNING.

AND YOU TRY AND HOLD ON TO THAT FADING HOPE FOR A LITTLE WHILE LONGER.

IN THE END I MOVED BACK TO MY DAD'S AND BACK TO THE TOWN I THOUGHT I ESCAPED.

4 YEARS SEEMS LIKE A LIFETIME AGO.

JUST LIKE THAT IT ALL RESETS. SAME HOUSE, SAME STAIRS...

... SAME BED.

I'VE GONE BACK TO THE START.

BACK TO A LIFE WITHOUT HER.
A LIFE WITHOUT ANNA.
MY SWEDISH BEAUTY.
NO LONGER MINE.

...
DING!
20:02
Anna
NIRVANA
Okay.
21 Apr 2011 21:19
This is so weird.....:(
Send

TAP
TAP
TAP

WYOOP.
20:03
Anna
This is so weird....:(
No? Not happy? It's the first night, the first night is always the worst.
Send

DILANG!
IVING
OOM
BOOKS

Yeah it's just all so weird. I didn't think I'd feel so sad.
TAP
TAP

It's been a really long ordeal. Two months of unease and unhappiness isn't going to change overnight.
When you get settled you'll love it there.
NIRVANA
TAP
TAP

I hope so.
I really miss what we had.
TAP
TAP

Me too. I miss it everyday.

I wish we'd not messed it up.

Yeah I wish we could have worked at fixing us. Wish we could have seen the signs earlier.
Maybe one day we can have another shot.
NIRVA

Yeah maybe. The one thing I'm worried about is we'll fall out and not be friends.

Well we don't know that do we? I might be quiet with you but that's because I'm hurting.
NIRVANA

Yeah I know. Oh dear. Very emotional.
Would we have it any other way?
NIRVANA

Heh. I guess not.
Hey I love you.
Hope you're okay.
NIRVANA

Love you too.

THANKS TO FAMILY ELLERBY, TOMAS & GUNNEL
ADAM CADWELL, MATTHEW SHERET, LIZZ LUNNEY
DAVID THOMAS, TOM HUNT, MATTHEW PROSSER
JOE LIST, JAMIE S. RICH, KIERON GILLEN
AND ALL MY FRIENDS AND FOES WHO DIDN'T
MIND ME DRAWING THEM INTO THIS BOOK (OR
DIDN'T SAY ANYTHING IF THEY DID...)

PROOF READING BY MERYL TRUSSLER

SPECIAL THANKS TO JEFFREY BROWN, JAMES KOCHALKA,
LIZ PRINCE AND CRAIG THOMPSON WHO DO THIS SORT
OF THING BETTER THAN ME.

MARC ELLERBY HAS DRAWN COMICS FOR PUBLISHERS SUCH AS ONI PRESS (LOVE THE WAY YOU LOVE) IMAGE COMICS (PUT THE BOOK BACK ON THE SHELF, THIS IS A SOUVENIR, PHONOGRAM THE SINGLES CLUB B-SIDE) AND ALSO BOOM! STUDIOS (CBGBs & OMFUG)

HE IS THE CREATOR OF CHLOE NOONAN: MONSTER HUNTER WHICH YOU CAN READ SOME OF AT CHLOENOONAN.COM

ELLERBISMS IS HIS DEBUT GRAPHIC NOVEL.
IT TOOK HIM FOREVER TO FINISH.

HE LIVES IN ESSEX, ENGLAND. HE'S NOT SURE WHY.

MARCELLERBY.COM
MARCLRB@GMAIL.COM
@MARCELLERBY
FACEBOOK.COM/MARCELLERBY